Shoot Feeding & Sericultural Trends

SHOOT FEEDING & SERICULTURAL TRENDS

by

Dr. T.V. Sathe

Department of Zoology,
Entomology Division,
Shivaji University, Kolhapur-416004, India

&

Dr. S.H. Thite

B.P. College, Angar, Mohol, Distt. Solapur

2004

DAYA PUBLISHING HOUSE
DELHI-110 035

ISBN   81-7035-326-2

Published by	:	**Daya Publishing House**
		1123/74, Deva Ram Park
		Tri Nagar, Delhi-110 035
		Phone : 27103999
		Fax : (011) 27199029
		E-mail : dayabooks@vsnl.com
		Website : www.dayabooks.com
Showroom	:	4762-63/23, Ansari Road
		New Delhi - 110 002
		Ph.: 23245578, 23244987
Laser Composed by	:	**Vaishnav Graphics & Systems**
		New Delhi - 110 055
Printed at	:	**Chawla Offset Printers**
		Delhi-110 052

PRINTED IN INDIA

PREFACE

Sericulture is an important agroforest based industry and good source of earning a foreign exchange and providing gainful employment. According to FAO approximately 35-40 countries have been involved in sericulture industry development in the world. More than half of these countries are situated in Asia (China, India, Thailand, Japan, North Korea, South Korea, Vietnam, Myanmar, Philippines, Taiwan, Sri Lanka, Bangladesh, Indonesia, Malaysia, Laos, Cambodia, Iran, Nepal, Afghanistan etc.) and more than 85-90 percent of raw silk/silk yarn has been produced by the five major silk producing countries such as China, India, Japan, Korea (North/South) and Thailand. However, the recent trend of silk production in each country has not been much changed except sharp decrease in Japan and South Korea in 1990s. Asia is most suitable for sericulture development and the largest region for cocoon/silk production among the four major regions of the world.

India has the distinction of being bestowed by nature with all the commercial known varieties of silk viz. mulberry, tasar, eri and muga. The overall mulberry silk production of the country for the year 2001 to 2002 was 15845 mt. Besides raw silk, India produces annually about 588 tons of spun silk yarn and 262 tons of noil-yarn. China ranks 1st and India ranks IInd in raw silk production in the world. However, there is always a demand supply gap of about 5000 mt. of raw silk. This clearly indicates that there is a wide scope for sericultural practices in India. From Maharashtra, Kolhapur, Sangli and Solapur districts have a great potential in sericultural practices. These districts are vary climatically and geographically. Biotic and abiotic factors play a very significant role in success or failure of rearing silkworms. Hence, in the present text attempts have been made to assess rearing and cocoon production of mulberry silkworms with respect to biotic and abiotic factors in southern Maharashtra. In addition, silkworm rearing techniques have been described with respect to traditional methods and recent methods including shoot feeding. Ecological aspects and different trends in rearing silkworms have been specially emphasized in the book. We hope that the book will be useful for sericulturists, students, teachers and researchers.

Dr. T.V. Sathe
Dr. S.H. Thite

Contents

CONTENTS

1
GENERAL INTRODUCTION

There are several significant achievements in different crops related to breeding either genetically higher in productivity or possessing resistance to various biotic and abiotic traces. The compound growth rate of various food crops/ commodities during the last 40 years has been fairly impressive, but it was poor in non food crops like forest plantation, mulberry etc.

India made tremendous progress in traditional agricultural practices. The number of promising varieties released during the last ten years clearly indicates that the pace of variety development in different crops and commodities has been quite encouraging. Variety resistant to major diseases and pests, also to saline/alkaline and drought conditions have been developed in all the important crops. (Rao, 1996).

Hybrid cotton, H4 commercialized by India is the 1st in the world. India is also the 1st country to produce hybrid castor and hybrid pigeon pea and the advances made in hybrid maize are in no way less significant than elsewhere in the world (Paroda, 1993). In sorghum, excellent hybrids namely CSH_1, CSH_5, CSH_6, CSH_9 have been evolved which are covering large areas of India and have demonstrated their superiority under a rainfed conditions. In pulses, a number of varieties within proven inbuilt resistance to various diseases have been evolved.

In case of rice tremendous varietal options do exist now to enhance yield on farmer's field. It is well known fact that wheat high yielding Indian dwarf varieties, helped India to achieve Green Revolution (Paroda, 1993).

The vision of future India will only depend on the recognition of "Science and technology" the greatest gift of God to humanity, and its proper application can initiate sustainable integrated development to ensure, food, economics and health security to all the people in the country (Rao, 1996). On the global basis during the last two hundred years total cultivated land area has increased from 600 million ha to 1500 million ha. Even though estimate indicates that the cultivable land across the global can be increased from the present 1500 million ha to about 2100 million ha through reclamation of degraded and waste land, the possibility of addition to arable land in Asia including India is less than 10% (Rao, 1996). However land for cultivation for mulberry have not increased significantly in India.

Indian sericulture is one of the important agro and forest based industry, earning a foreign exchange of Rs. 2235.38 crores/annum (year 2000-2002) and providing gainful employment to over 6 million people. Sericulture is rearing of silkworms either on mulberry or non mulberry plants for production of silk.

Soil erosion in deforested areas in our country ranges from 10 ton/ha in the plains to about 30 ton/ha in the North-Eastern hilly regions, ten to fifty times larger than in the forested areas. The resulting annual sedimentation load from Ganga and Bramhaputra alone exceed 1500 million tons, making them the two largest dumpers of suspended load anywhere in the world. The environmental problems caused by increased sedimentation has extensively affected the capacity of reservoirs, the aquatic ecosystems in the inland waters, soil erosion, in fertility, recharging capacity, and underground water level. Extensive deforestation has resulted in increased carbon dioxide concentration in the atmosphere, increased albed from deforested areas altering the energy balance between the terra-ferma and the atmosphere, increased run off of rain precipitation from 20% to almost 50% and a gradual extinction of bio diversity. Mulberry cultivation can protect the soil erosion and even flora and fauna of the target area.

Deforestation, pressure of population and increased industrialization have reduced our total forest cover to just 20%

of the land area, only half of which is closed forest carrying over 40% canopy. In the National policy adopted in 1952, it is recommended that 33% forest should cover across the country with 60% in hilly areas (Rao, 1996). Deforestation results in increased run off rain water, precipitation and extensive soil erosion, resulting in unacceptable deterioration of top soil, degradation of top soil, degradation of land and sedimentation of water bases resulting in desertification and frequent flooding.

Over the past few years, a more comprehensive view of environment has grown which brought within the ambit of our relating to resource management, pollution and waste management, and human settlements. The resource management covers depletion of non-renewable resources, fossil fuel, degradation and over consumption of renewable resources, biomass and soil, destruction of genetic resources, desertification and deforestation etc. Sericulture in deforested and other areas would certainly add relevance in improving the situation of soil erosion and deforestation of the country by planting mulberry.

For checking the migration of people to urban conglomerates a significant increase in rural income and employment opportunities is of great importance. In spite of the country is self-sufficiency in food, the absurd concept of rural economy based on the sale of raw agricultural products has led to the deplorable situation of the per capita income of the rural poor continuing to remain just one fifth of that of his urban counterpart. Sericulture provides wonderful opportunity for employment to the rural landless people and to check migration. It also provides opportunity for utilising the waste water and dry lands and for handsome money to the poor rural marginal farmers. Where nothing is grown in a depleted land, mulberry can found successful.

Natural forest policy says that 33% of the land should be covered with forest to maintain the ecosystem. India has only 20.19% of the total land area under forest. Recent remote sensing aerial photography has shown that the percentage declined to 12%. This shrinkage in forest area is due to the onslaughts of fire wood gatherers, land hungry farmers and industrial timber interests. Rapid population growth is another factor causing the depletion of forest, reminding one of the remark. "The forest came before the civilization and deserts after it."

India is steadily losing more than 1.5 million ha out of 11 million ha of world topical forests land each year. In other words, once every five years forest cover of the size of the state of Haryana vanishers and over three decades, would equals an area of about the size of India. Hence, social forestry programme is the need of the hour. The term sericulture is not merely rearing and production of silk from mulberry silkworm, *Bombyx mori* L. but also from non mulberry silkworms. Plantation of mulberry in fallow/barren land will certainly strengthen the bulk of green area upto some extent.

Mulberry plants are tolerant and cultivable to a wide range of agro-climatic conditions. The agro-forestry is a sustainable land management system in which a woody perernnial is raised in conjunction with arable crops and/or live stock, either in sequence or simultaneously on the same piece of land. On the basis of agro-ecology and socioeconomy, major systems of agroforestry, Nair (1988) reported are as follows :

(1) Shifting cultivation (2) Taungya cultivation (3) Home-gardening or multitier system (4) Agro-Sericulture system (5) Sericulture system (6) Silvi pastoral system (7) Alley cropping or hedge row system (8) Agri-Silvi horticulture and (9) Wind break and shelter bels.

Mulberry can be grown in all above agroecosystems. (Singh and Ghosh, 1992).

Sericulture is an admixture of forestry, agriculture, industry and art. It is well known as a highly employment oriented and a low capital intensive activity, and an effective tool for rural development with overwhelming number of advantages. It transfers wealth from richer sections of society to poorer since, silk is consumed mostly by affluent people and the money so spent on purchases of silk is distributed among the sericulturists, reelers, twisters, weavers and traders, with 51.5%, 6.2%, 8.2%, 14.5% and 19.5% respectively (Nair, 1988). Sericulture industry, employing 51.52 lakh persons mostly in the rural areas. Thus, it prevents migration of rural population to urban. It provides highest employment opportunities (25.23 lakh persons per year) as compared to other occupations. Sericulture creates employment at all the stages viz. mulberry cultivation (5.20 lakh), silkworm rearing (5.83 lakh) reeling (0.71 lakh) and weaving (7.23 lakh).

Tasar sericulture is also playing important role in industrial development. Tasar rearers mostly belongs to various tribes and are the weaker sections of our society, mostly living in remote forests. The tribals account for nearly 8.10% of countrys' population (Census, 1991). Out of the total tribal population of 38 million, over 97% are confined to the rural areas mostly inhabiting the forest belts. Nearly 30 million (77%) are located in tasar cultivating states of tropical (25.67 million) and temperate (4.23 million) tasar belts (Census, 1991).

The states Bihar, Madhya Pradesh, Orissa, Maharashtra, Andhra Pradesh, Karnataka, West Bengal and Uttar Pradesh comes under tasar belt. In all 15 states are engaged in the production of non-mulberry silk. Bihar is the largest producer of tasar cocoons. Madhya Pradesh is second and Orissa ranks third in cocoon production. Madhya Pradesh has 40 lakh tribal population in tasar cultivating districts and the area under tasar food plants is also vast (50.44 lakh ha). Eastern and Southern parts of the districts Bilaspur, Raigarh, Sargunja, Balghat, Mandala and Bastar are actively engaged in tasar culture. The district Bilaspur is one of the traditional tasar districts of Madhya Pradesh with rich tribal population and forests. (Siddiqui and Omkar, 1987).

Benchamin and Jolly (1987) says that the industry holds high promise as an employment intensive occupation specially in rural and semi-urban areas. Sericulture has been identified as an occupation of low investment, high output source of employment and income. Unemployment and underemployment continue to be the major problems of our country, it is more serious in rural areas. Out of 306 million people living below poverty line in India, 249 million are rural areas and only 57 million in Urban centers. 70% of the total workforce is still depend upon agriculture sector for their livelihood. Despite considerable industrialization, this figure has remained more or less constant during the past two decades. In labour surplus economy and worth while planning strategy should have maximization of employment opportunities at one of its key objectives. Benchamin and Jolly (1987) says that sericulture industry fits into our socioeconomic condition as a tool for rural development. Out of the 5.76% lakhs villages in the country, sericulture is practised in more than 70,000 villages, providing employment to more than 60 lakh people in rural and semi urban areas. It is estimated that one acre of mulberry provides gainfull employment opportunities indirectly in units like manufacture of equipments and marketing of agricultural products. Rural economy in India is largely dependent on agriculture. There is a considerable scope to increase employment and income in rural areas through labour intensive remunerative enterprises like apiculture, lacculture and sericulture. However, sericulture industry is unique in its advantages and suitability to the rural development.

Sericulture can play a very crucial role by providing the job opportunities. A very large part of rural woman population is underemployed in India in total labour population, women constitute about 48%, traditional job is insignificant for the fulfilment of requirement of rural women's. Even if a family has some land, the woman works on the other field to supplement their family income. Yet, the woman has very little say regarding the use of her earnings. Mechanization in the business also pushing women labour into the unskilled category. This entire process ensures the continued marginalisation of woman. However, sericulture, an income generating activity can provide multiple advantages to women, (1) She can do at home, woman gets a fairer deal from the economy for less effort, she earns more. (2) She can combine this work with her other duties. (3) She can control, her timing. (4) She can control her own earnings, the harder she works, more she earns. (5) She is ensured for a year round income. (6) She learns to deal with people outside her home community/ village and develops her won personality.

60% of the worker force engaged in sericulture is said to be women. Rural women sericulturists have to be strengthened as production to help them to increase productivity and returns. In this, instance women have to be reached with credit, access to resources such as land, inputs, technology, training, information, as well as the materials with which they can become sustainable producer (Venugopal, 1994). Women can supplement the other business like intercropping and introducing stall fed cattle, sheep, rabbits and open fed poultry for additional income from the parental crop mulberry. It is commonly recognized that women, in all traditional sericultural states, constitutes a substantial proportion (53%) of the total work force in sericulture and contribute vitally to the sectors of silkworm rearing, reeling of cocoon and even in twisting, wearing, printing and dying (Gayathri Devi, 1994). In India, at present more than 75000 women are activity engaged in sericultural activities. In sericultural industry mulberry and non-mulberry silk is produced by rearing of silkworms. In India, all the four varieties of silk, mulberry, Tasar, Eri and Muga are produced.

The silkworm belongs to the order Lepidoptera. Silkworms are grouped on the basis of their feeding habits and domestication. Silk produced by the silkworms have different names, given on the basis of feeding, host plant. Silkworms belong to super family Bombycidae. However, *B. mori* comes under the family Bombycidae. The members of silkworms which produce commercial value silk are given below along with their families.

1) *Bombyx mori* Linn.
   (Domesticated mulberry silkworm)   Bombycidae

2) *Bombyx madarina* (Wild ancestor of mulberry silkworm)   Bombycidae

3) *Antheraea pernyi* G.M. (Air Chinese tasar silkworm)   Saturniidae

4) *Antheraea mylitta* Drury (It is a Indian tasar silkworm)   Saturniidae

5) *Antheraea yamamai* G.M. (Air Japanese tasar silkworm)   Saturniidae

6) *Philosamia cynthia* D. (A wild species of Eri silkworm)   Saturniidae

7) *Philosamia ricinl* Boised (The eri silkworm)   Saturniidae

8) *Eriogyna pyretorum* (Fishline silkworm Hainan Island)   Saturniidae

Out of the four types of silk produced in India the mulberry silk is commercially the most important and it constitutes about 95% of the world production and is a most commonly known and commercially available silk in the global market. Mulberry silk is produced from *B. mori* by rearing the worms on mulberry leaves. A very large number of mulberry varieties are known to science (Dandin, 2002).

Mulberry can be grown in temperate and tropical zones of the world with different environmental conditions. More than 60 countries are involved in cultivation of mulberry for cocoon production of silkworms. Mulberry is medium sized deciduous plant belonging to family *Moraceae*. More than one thousand varieties have been reported from Japan. While, 798 have been reported from India (Dhandin and Ramesh, 1987). Mulberry is cultivated in 227586 hectares in India. Out of which 2,16764 ha. mulberry is under irrigation in South India (Dandin and Ramesh, 1987). In the year 2001-2002 mulberry was cultivated in 231372 hectares in India (Dandin, 2002).

China ranks first in the world for raw silk production, which accounts for two-third of total cocoon and silk production. Most parts of China receive moderately high rainfall and the temperature ranges between 10-20°C. Mulberry is grown as monocrop and to some extent as burder or tree.

Mulberry is mainly planted through grafts which is carried out during March to April. Mulberry is generally resistance to pests and diseases and also adverse, conditions. In China, out of 26 species, reported, 14 species are distributed with more than 2000 germplasm varieties. It currently has about 40 good commercial mulberry varieties adopted to various areas. Husang 32, Husang 197 and 7, the main varieties, belongs to *Morus latifolia*. Recently, evolved varieties such as Yu2, Yu237, are quite popular in China. The promising mulberry varieties like gloody big flower are common tree (border) varieties grown on sichuam province of China. Mulberry varieties have been evolved to suit different agroclimatic conditions. Lunjiao belongs to *M. atropulparea* is suited for southern sub-tropics (Pearl river area), cook comb mulberry and black Lu mulberry for yellow river area and Shandong provine while heigelu and bolo mulberry varieties for shanxi and Heben region.

Govindaiah *et al.* (1997) opines that region specific mulberry varieties need to be develop in India. Mulberry, belongs to the family 'Moraceae' in plant kingdom. Further, it belor *s* to the genus *Morus* Linnaeus. Broadly, the mulberry is classified as white mulberry (*M. alba*) black mulberry (*M. nigra*) red mulberry (*M. rubra*), Indian mulberry (*M. indica*) and Russian mulberry (*M. tatarica*). Recently, mulberry is classified into 30 species with numerous varieties. *M. nigral,* and *M. alba* and the wild species such a *M. alba,* var. *indica* (L) Bur. (*M. indica* L.) *M. serrata* Roxb. and *M. macroura* Mig. (*M. lavigata* Wall. ex Brandis) are prominent Indian species. The Indian wild species are found in the lower Himalayan belt upto an elevation of '9000' feet (MSL) from Kashmir to Assam. Oldest Known mulberry tree is identified as *M. serrata* and the tree is located at Joshi Math (UP) on the way to Badrinath in the Himalayas. This has a girth of 28 feet and is 1400 years old. Shri Adishankaracharya is known to have medicated under this tree and later on established one of the four mutts of the Adwita Cult at this place. Thus, it is a religious and sacred tree. In the kumaon and Sivalik hills numerous natural varieties of mulberry are found as a part of the forest flora. Himalayan belt is believed to be the centre of the origin of mulberry in India.

Camararius in 1985 first demonstrated sex in the mulberry which laid foundation for plant breeding. Surprisingly, the sex expression in mulberry has remained a 'puzzle' for scientists. For the purpose of mulberry improvement programme, the wild varieties and the hybrid stocks are essential. Japanese have accumulated as many as 1,250 types of mulberry. The genus *Morus* is represented by four species and several varieties in India. About 80 species are scattered through out the world. Presently, the collection of mulberry in India is around 798 types, of which 320 are preserved at central sericultural Research and Training Institute, Mysore (Dandin and Ramesh, 1987). However, in Maharashtra very few varieties M-5 (Fig. 1), V-I (Fig. 3) and S-36 (Fig. 4) are practised many times local varieties of mulberry are also tried (Fig. 2).

In several states of India including Maharashtra, mulberry is cultivated in row system and paired row system. (Figs. 5, 6 and 7). Mulberry is the only food for rearing of *B. mori* hence, mulberry cultivation has a very vital role in sericulture. Leaf quality and yield determines the quality and quantity of the cocoons.

Mulberry is very useful plant. It has direct relation with the silk. It is also useful as fodder source, fire wood, timber for building houses and boats, for preparation of sport goods, furniture, fancy items and as medicine. Mulberry fruits are edible. This plant has medicinal value. Mulberry contains different chemicals of medicinal value in different parts of plant viz. leaf, fruit, stem, seed and root etc. In the form of decoctions and

PLATE 1

Fig. 1 : Mulberry M-5 Variety   Fig. 2 : Mulberry Local Variety
Fig. 3 : Mulberry V-1 Variety   Fig. 4 : Mulberry S-36 Variety

PLATE 2

Fig. 5 : Paired row system with drip irrigation

Fig. 6 : Sara system of mulberry plantation

Fig. 7 : Row system of mulberry plantation

concoctions several chemical substance are normally extracted into aqueous media.

Leaf juice has special quality of moisturizing and keeps the skin smooth and healthy, prevents throat infections, irritation and inflammation in the throat, useful in preventing high fever as febrifuge in endemic malaria. It can also prevent diarrhoea and cold. Hence, used in the preparation of syrup which possesses refrigerant and laxative - properties and laxative for infants. For the diabetics and high blood pressure patients mulberry leaf juice is quite effective.

As a vegetable it is accepted by humans just like pea, cucumber and drum stick leaves. The green leaves of above plants are more nutritive and mulberry leaves satisfy the dietary requirement of human beings and contain all the elements required for the body, vitamin A, B, C, and D are in sufficient quantity in mulberry leaves. However vitamin C is rich. The growing mulberry leaves contain 6 to 6.8% crude protein, 4% soluble carbohydrates and 0.6% crude fat and also several compounds of calcium, phosphorus, iron, copper, zinc etc. According to Sreekumar *et al.* (1994) to produce 3000 calories of energy the recommended daily diet is 70 gm of protein, 0.8 gm of calcium, 10 mg. of iron, 500 Iu of vitamin A, 1.6 mg. of BI, 1.8 mg. of B2, 75 mg. of C and 400 Iu of D.

Mulberry waste leaves are used as fodder. Leaf contains crude protein 13.53, crude fat 3.53 and crude fibre 13.73 Iu. Cattle feed on mulberry and leaf over shoot have been found to improve their milk yield. Mulberry leaves are also valuable source of vitamin and improve the health of poultry birds and increase egg production. Chlorophy II extracted from leaf is used for cosmetics viz. soap, hair oil, and also tooth paste and medicine in India.

Mulberry stem is useful as fencing material, medium grade fuel wood, preparing baskets and waste shoots are used in compost. Aqueour and alkali extracts of stem and leaves are activate against gram positive bacteria and yeasts. In China and Europe stem bark stripped from waste branches are used for paper pulp. The bark is used as vermifuge and purgative.

On account of its elasticity and flexibility, the mulberry wood is used mainly for the manufacture of sport goods. It is compared with teak because of shock resistant ability, strength, hardness etc. Hockey sticks, tennis rackets, presses, cricket stamps, home building, agricultural implement, furniture, tool handles, potes, shafts and bent parts of carriage and carts are prepared from timber of mulberry. Wood is also used for small boats and large ships. Mulberry wood contains tannin which is useful for tanning and colouring purpose (Sreekumar *et al*, 1994).

Mulberry seed contains 25 to 35% of a yellow dying oil with sp.gr. 150.924 to 0.926. Liquid fatty acids constitute the major part (80-90%) of the total fatty acids of the oil. Yellow dye obtained from the roots are used in dying process. The bark of root is bitter and acts as cathartic, antihelmintic and stringent. In China also it is used as restorative tonic and as remedy for nervous disorders.

AIDS is burning problem of humans at global level. Mulberry contain some components useful for controlling HIV. An alkaloid deoxyjirmycin (DNJ) has been extracted from the root bark of the black mulberry, *M. nigra*, which resembles glucose and interferes with the synthesis of sugar chain. This chemical hinders the addition of sugar molecules to the outer coat of the human immuno-deficiency virus. The surface glycoprotein of HIV is rich in sugar chain and is involved in the budding activity of the virus on and from a cell. DNJ inhibits the enzymes *glycosidases*, responsible for trimming the sugar chains on glycoproteins. It means, DNJ hinders the docking of HIV on the human cell and hence, makes the attack futile. Thus DNJ, is easy to synthesize and seems to be a promise as a potential medicine against AIDS (Ray, 1989), Butyl-DNJ is reported more active in treating AIDS. According to Ray (1989) and Tewary and Rao (1990) GD Searle Pharmaceuticals company is working on DNJ and have collaboration with chemists from Oxford and Cambridge.

During the last century, the silk industry has greatly contributed to the foreign exchange earnings. Among the various developing countries, silk still offers the economic prosperity. On the other hand, wild silks are not very popular, although Chinese tasar (*A. pernii*), Indian tasar (*A. mylitta*), Eri silk (*P. ricini*), Muga silk (*A. assama*) and Tensan (*A. yammai*) have long been used for characteristic silk textiles, forming a small segment of the market (Hiromu, 1998). Recent research on tasar silk exposed some beneficial aspects that tasar silk is helpful in controlling cholesterol in hemolymph, antibacterial functions and have role in UV absorption effect. The international society for wild silkworms (ISWSM), Japan has initiated research on wild silkmoths and silks (Hiromu, 1998). In Maharashtra wild silkworms have been surveyed by Sathe *et al.* (2001) and Sathe and Jadhav (2001) contributed on rearing technique for *A. mylitta*.

The people living in the forests and adjacent rural areas are highly dependent on the plants and their products for their daily needs including food and medicine (Yadav *et al.* 1997).

As regards to mulberry silk, China, India, Japan, CIS block and Brazil are the major raw-silk producers of the world. Sericulture is also practised in other Asian countries like Thailand, Malaysia and Vietnam. China accounted 63% (48, 500 mt) of the world silk production (76,761 mt) in 1991, recent (year – 2002) account is 15845 mt.

In recent years, with modernization of equipment and increasing demand for quality and productivity, large scale farming or corporate involvement has entered in sericulture. Different approaches have been involved in improving cocoon quality from the countries like Japan, China, Thailand, Malaysia, Brazil, South Korea, Vietnam and Indonesia.

The sericultural technology of Japan is considered to be one of the best in the world and could be beneficial to many developing countries. Grainage activity are governed by private agencies in Japan, young age rearing is conducted under controlled environment in co-operative rearing houses, and chawki mechanized rearing is the specialized aspect of rearing. Late age worms are supplied to farmers for rearing in individual rearing shades. Co-operative have tie-ups with reeling factories for marketing of cocoons co-operate houses are also involved in supplying machinery, silkworm eggs and sericulture know-how.

Japan has sericultural farms in 40% of its municipalities. In many of these districts, cocoon is an important farm product. The countries climate as well as the hard working nature and dexterity of the Japanese farmer helped Japan to come up in sericulture. Surprisingly, silkworm rearing has long been the countries characteristic and seems considerable improvement in its technology. Japanese farmer with annual income of less than five million yen generally earn additional income from non-farm jobs to continue farm management and thus, part time farmers are increasing but the number of sericulturists found decreasing.

As like India, Chinese silkworm eggs are produced by government grainages and distributed to government agencies who in turn sell them to large government owned reeling factories. Sericulture machinery industry is government owned. China exports silkworm eggs, cocoons, raw silk yarn, fabrics and ready made garments, through government agencies to the world.

Thailand ranks 5th in world for raw silk production. In Thailand grainage activities are performed by both the government and private agencies. The seeds are also imported from Japan, Taiwan and China. Reeling factories conduct chawki rearing and provides late age worms for rearing to farmers with buy back arrangement for cocoon. In some cases mulberry farms belong to the reeling factory are given to farmers for cultivation and rearing of silkworms. Ready made garments, cocoon and raw-silk yarn etc are exported by Thailand.

In Brazil production of silkworm eggs is mainly by private grainages. Young age rearing is on co-operative basis and under controlled and mechanized conditions. Late age rearing is conducted by large reeling factories. Brazil exports cocoons and raw silk yarn.

In Indonesia cocoons are produced by individual farmers or corporative farms of 300-500 acres. However silkworm eggs are imported from Japan. For demonstration of mulberry cultivation, silkworm rearing units are constructed to the technology to local farmer. There is joint participation of the government and the corporate sector in sericultural activities.

Malaysia import silkworm eggs from Japan. Activation of mulberry, rearing of silkworm and reeling are under one roof. Most of projects are government owned, Malaysia exports cocoons. In South Korea, exports raw silk yarn, sericulture machinery and project know-how. Vietnam is emerging as a silk yarn producer and exporter due to government support. Government owned reeling factories buy cocoons from farmers in Vietnam.

Philippines sericulture has recent origin. Though, the beginning was made prior to the 2nd world war, the industry could not survive, due to lack of technical and financial support. The Government of Philippines is having a few aid schemes to encourage the people to take up the sericulture. The farmers are encouraged technically and financially from Philippines Textile Research Institute, (PTRI) and ministry of human settlement Philippines respectively (CSB, 1985).

From European Union countries, France is leading silk processor. For centuries, the French city of Lyon has been producing fabrics of the highest quality for domestic consumption and for export as well. France is famous for designing fabrics, and serves the fashion-houses of prominent centres like Paris continued to be important customers. France importing around 15.2% silk fabrics and woven silk fabrics is about 14.7% from European Union countries. The French wearing industry which was backing on domestic supplies of raw silk is now dependent entirely on imports. French industry imported 424 tons of raw silk in 1995 from China and from Brazil 365 tons in 1996. The total imports of silk and silk products has found a steady increase from 1638 tons in 1991 to 2067 tons in 1995. France has got a reputation for high quality fashionable exclusive goods. The unit prices of France exports of silk goods are considerably higher as compared to Korea and Italy.

The association of French silk traders (Inter-soie France) established in 1995 is actively engaged in involving the problems of international silk trade. In addition, the project EUROCHRYSALIDE is encouraging to develop high technology sericulture and expanding silk production at global level.

Thanks are due to Siling-ti for her greatest discovery, 'Silk' Industrious Chinese used the silk not only as a new means of employment but also as the most valuable commodity in the world trade. This art of 'making silk' was guarded as a top most secret for more than 3000 years. Kivsur (2001) demonstrated the world silk route recently.

By the period of Han dynasty (founded in 200A.D.) China has established a flourishing silk trade with western countries. The countless carvans made their route across Asia bringing silk from China to Damascus – the then world market centre. From there, it was taken to Rome and further, others bought it paying fabulous sums.

While China was the source of silk, Damascus turned into a world silk market where East and West exchanged their goods. The Persian took the lead of bringing silk from China. And thus they adopted commanding position in this trade and controlled all the silk that came from China. They exploited the peoples craze for silk into gold coins. The legendary fabric was sold by them at such - fabulous prices that the price itself turned into a legend! They had to pay by their nose. The Roman emperor Justinian had to file objection for paying such exorbitant prices to Persians but in vain. During the sixth century, the determined emperor even tried to find out a new trade route to China via Constantinople keeping away Persia. For different reasons it was not successful. But he did not lose his heart. He sent two Nestorian monks to China (who had earlier lived there) to 'smuggle' the secret of 'silk making'. In a most astonishing way, these intelligent monks brought back this 'secret' to Constantinople risking their life. In the history, it has been regarded as one of the greatest 'successful spying mission'. Along with the 'secret' these monks also had brought with them some mulberry seeds and silkworm eggs hidden in their hollow clubs. This greatest industrial espionage ended the monopoly of both China and Persia as producer and trader of silk respectively. During the next few centuries, people from various countries learnt the art of 'silk making'. While Muslim introduced silkworms to Spain and Sicily during 800-990s. Italy turned into an epicenter of western silk market by 1200. The enterprising French took up silk wearing during 1500. The first silk weaving factory was built at Mansfield conn in England in 1810.

During 400 A.D., a Chinese princess who got married to an Indian prince brought with her some seeds of mulberry and silkworm eggs by hiding them in the lining of her head gear. Sericulture was first established in the tract which lies between the Ganges and Brahmaputra rivers in India. Though there is no recorded document available regarding the origin of silk in India prior to 400 AD, one can find the mention of silk in the Indian epics like Ramayana and Mahabharata which adds mystery to the history of silk in India. However, one cannot deny the fact that sericulture and silk has been a part of Indian tradition and culture.

Sericulture reached Japan by Korea during the early part of the fourth century. If others smuggled the secret of silk to their countries, four Chinese concubines were brought to Japan to teach them the making of woven silk! With the time, Japanese perfected the art much so that they had been number two position in the world silk production, till recently. The silk route in reality was an all purpose trade route traversing to the west from the orient and to the East by the Middle East.

The silk route was highly hazardous, treacherous to anyone especially the traders. Starting from 'Xian of shaanxi province of China, it traversed through mountains and deserts; central Asia to Tyre; to Europe and Egypt and further to port cities by sea. From Mediterranean it spread to Spain, Latin America and North America. California seems to be the end point of this famous route. It almost stretched round the global.

Today, silk and silk making are no more a secret. The whole world knows about it. Presently sericulture is very popularly practised in dozens of countries of the world. Countries like India, Japan, China have international institutions/training centres to teach sericulture. However, with all these, China has not allowed any other country to surpass its first position in the world in silk production.

Sericulture is an ancient industry in India, references to 'silk' may be traced back to age old sacred Hindu epics. Historical records indicate the existence of a flourishing export trade in silk good between India and Europe in the second century B.C. During the regime of Kanishka in 58 B.C., silk was exported from India to Rome. During Moghul regime the industry was in flourishing stage.

According to some Indian Scholars silkworms were first domesticated in the foothills of Himalaya. It is well-known fact that the British East India company gave the fillip to sericulture in India by developing many silk centres in the country. Company exported large quantity of silk to England from West Bengal. The major silk producing states recognized were Mysore, Jammu and Kashmir (FAO, 1987).

It is believed that sericulture was introduced to India in 130 B.C. However it remained confined only to the Bramhaputra valley in West Bengal and Kashmir. But Tippu Sultan who had introduced silk in Mysore and thus, Karnataka has been emerged as the largest silk producing state in India.

Karnataka, Andhra Pradesh, Tamil Nadu, West Bengal and Jammu Kashmir are the major contributors to the development of sericulture industry and silk production in India. The Karnataka state is macro contributor, 64% and Andhra Pradesh 18.5% (Anonymous, 1998). The major advantage to Karnataka state is that, farmers get timely technical support from Central Silk Board and various research institutes located in the state. The actual development of sericulture in Karnataka has taken five decades to attain the present status.

Sericulture industry of Karnataka is 200 years old. Tippu Sultan organized the industry in 1780. Karnataka has well established technological units related to mulberry cultivation, silkworm rearing, reeling, twisting and wearing. However, industry has undergone severe variance due to pests and diseases from time to time. In Karnataka, out of the cultivable area of about 14.0 million ha. mulberry is being grown in nearly 0.15 million ha. has accounting for 10.7% of the cultivable area. The CSB in April 1961, took over the state research institute and in 1965 merged the training institute. During the years 1961-80 efforts have been made to improve sericultural activities which resulted in production of improved hybrid local varieties and bivoltine hybrids. Races like Hosa Mysore, Pure Mysore, NB_4D_2 were evolved. M-5 mulberry variety tested for rearing. In 1979-80 two bivoltine races namely NB_7 and NB_{18} were released by CSR and TI Mysore to replace KA and NB_7. Due to introduction of high yielding mulberry varieties such as V_1, M-5 etc. and new bivoltine races and chawki rearing centres, silk production per unit area have been increased and renditta decreased. Silk production per ha. increased from 11.98 kg. to 24.35 kg. and the renditta was decreased from 17.5 to 13.43 kg.

Recently CSR and TI Mysore identified varieties of mulberry such as S-13, S-34 and AR-10 for rain dependent farming (Dandin Sarkar, 2002). Their performance is satisfactory.

Karnataka has favourable agroclimatic conditions for expansion of sericulture activities. In Karnataka the activities were confined to five traditional districts, Mysore, Kolar, Tumkur, Bangalore and Mandya. Due to confined region and extension support, the state created success stories. In Karnataka, silk production per ha. was 24.35 kg. and silk quality was below D grade in 1980 as compared to 133.47 kg. of A grade in Japan. Karnataka state was lacking certain basic factors to launch programme of production of bivoltine silk in a big way. Karnataka state launched two mega projects called KSP-I (1980-88) and KSP-II (1989-96) with world bank assistance. The project was objected for increasing raw silk production by about 1600 mt. of which 1000 mt. was to be bivoltine. In both the projects bivoltine incentive schemes were adopted but, bivoltine silk did not catch-up as contemplated in the project. The cocoon and silk production in Karnataka during 1993-94 was 70,208 and 8,250 tons respectively. Karnataka expect 1,80,000 ha of mulberry cultivation, 1,18,630 mt. of cocoon production and 13,732 mt. of silk production by 2000-2001 (Das Gupta, 1994).

In Andhra Pradesh, nearly 80% of the silk production comes from the districts Anantpur, Chittor, Karnool and Kadappa. At present, about 1.50 lakh acres of area is under mulberry cultivation and the raw silk production in the state was about 2250 mt. covering 60% of the farmers from small and marginal category. It is estimated that about 7 lakh families are dependent on sericulture in the state Andhra Pradesh expects 20000 acres of mulberry, 20 crores brushing of dfls, 100,000 tons of cocoon production including 10% bivottine, 12,500 mt. raw silk production, 1500 mt. bivoltine raw silk production, cocoon yield 65 k.g./100 dfls, renditta for Bi x Bi 5.5 to 6, and for Multivoltine x Bivoltine 7, by the year 2000-2001 (Bhide, 1994). Director of sericulture under the Ministry of Textiles is implementing and encouraging agencies for the overall development of sericulture in Andhra Pradesh. Through co-operative societies the state Government has also exposed various schemes to give boost to sericultural activities like technical support, financial support to sericulturists for workshed-cum-house for rural and urban weavers, modernization of looms, support to chawki rearing activity, marketing etc.

Tamil Nadu ranks 2nd in India in sericultural activities. Tamil Nadu has increased its mulberry silk production over the last five decades. During 1994-95 mulberry plantation was in 13,481 ha. area (Anonymous, 1998). The consumption of dfls was 107 lakhs, cocoon production 735/mt. production of raw silk 774 mt. no of Handlooms 60,000 and requirement of raw silk was 1600 mt. during 1996-97. The state government of Tamil Nadu has a very strong extension and promotion wing which promotes the sericultural activities by providing technical assistance. The co-optex, a co-operative society established by reelers and weavers also playing very important role in development of silk industry in Tamil Nadu by marketing raw silk and silk fabrics. In Tamil Nadu most of the sericulture activities are concentrated in five districts namely, Dharmapur, Madurai, Salem, Kanchipuram and Dindigad. The districts Kanchipuram, Arani, Salem and Khumbhakenan are very famous for producing cloth or sarees.

In Madhya Pradesh, sericulture activity comes under the ministry of Rural Development, hence taking lead in sericulture. A separate commissionerate is working for the development of sericulture activity in the state. The Government of Madhya Pradesh is implementing a big five years project on sericulture with a Grant-in-Aid from Japan Economic Co-operation Fund and technical assistance. By this project mulberry cultivation would increase by 6000 ha. and tasar activities by 2000 ha. Government has also proposed to purchase land for development of mulberry and tasar sericulture. Development of market infrastructure, creation of Technical Service Centres, one time subsidy to farmers, setting up of small co-operatives, involvement of NGOs, rearing of bivoltine by adopting modern technologies from Japan and Central Silk Board are worth while activities in sericulture by Madhya Pradesh.

Assam is the state in which all four commercial varieties of silk are produced. Assam is considered to be the primary epicenter for origin and spread of sericulture in the world (Anonymous, 1988). In the total annual raw silk production of India, Assam shares about 450 to 500 mt. and is one of the major silk producing state of India. Sericulture activities are carried out in almost all districts of Assam but, commercial silk weaving is concentrated in Sualkuchi of Kamrup district. Sericulture is a traditional activity and this business has its roots since ages. In Assam silk production is low due to poor technology, primitive cultural practices, non-commercialization of cocoon production and under developed marketing facilities. Among the four commercial varieties of silk reared in Assam, Muga is the glory of the state (Anonymous, 1988).

About 20,280 villages are engaged in sericultural activity in the North-Eastern region of India. Sericulture forms a part of tradition here, especially in the states of Assam, Manipur and Tripura. Attempts to develop sericulture in the hilly areas of

Nagaland, Mizoram and Arunachal Pradesh have yielded encouraging results.

West Bengal is one of the leading silk producing state in the country with a raw silk production of about 1,137 mt/year (Vijayan *et al.* 1998). Malda, Murshidabad and Birbhum are the major silk producing districts of West Bengal. In West Bengal silkworms are reared during 4-5 times in a year. The climatic conditions of the state are found not conducive for bivoltine silkworm rearing. The central sericultural research and training institute, Berhampore has identified certain genotypes for mulberry and boosted bivoltine sericulture in the region.

In Kashmir, sericulture is in existence since time immemorial and prior to 1897. It is traditional activity of J and K. The state has implemented a big project on sericulture costing Rs. 40 crores from the World Bank. In J and K mainly univoltine races are practised. Presently, area under mulberry plantation is more than 2750 ha. (Sathe and Jadhav, 2001). Silk reeling in Kashmir is carried out only by the government filatures. As like Kashmir implementation of bivoltine project in the Western Ghats of Maharashtra would worth while activity in sericulture.

Uttar Pradesh hills and the sub-Himalayan tracts (Tarai region) offer ideal climatic condition for mulberry cultivation and rearing of high quality bivoltine cocoons. The annual raw silk production was 15-20 mt. for the past many years in the state (Thomas, 1998). The government has proposed major silk project to produce 750 mt. of high quality raw silk with rising 8500 ha. of mulberry plantation in Uttar Pradesh (Thomas, 1998).

Maharashtra, Orissa, Bihar, Gujarat, Rajasthan, Meghalaya are also taking keen interest in the development of sericulture though they are recognized as non-traditional sericultural states.

Indian sericulture is widely accepted in the world and the country has already made good stride. Research contributions of CSR and IT, Mysore by way of introduction of improved mulberry varieties, and by silkworm rearing management under tropical condition, introducing on productive silkworm breeds helped to spread sericulture in wide agro-climatic areas (Datta, 1995). The production pace is slow as compared to the spread of sericulture and many sericultural states are not able to utilize the opportunity made available to them (Datta, 1995).

In spite of ranking IInd in global silk scenario, Indian sericulture remains primitive and is not able to come up with the production of high quality silk or fabrics on large scale (Datta, 1995). Multivoltine breeds are popular with farmers in India. The CSR and TI was successfully evolved high yielding bivoltine breeds through conventional breeding programme. The popularity of bivoltine breeds remains dismal due to poor survivability in the adverse tropical agro-climatic conditions coupled with diseases caused due to continuous silkworm rearing. This situation is further worsened by poor cultivation practices, rearing management, scanty ground water and soil types (Datta, 1995). However, recent investigations (Dandin, 2002) facilitated successful use of bivoltine with good results. Yadav (2002) highlighted major research activities carried out in CSBR and D institutions during the recent years (2001-2002).

New opportunities for crop, tree and animal improvement by genetic combination are now available which in turn, has created new prospects for skilled employment in villages through manufacture of bio-fertilizer, bio-pesticides, bio-control measures and establishment of biomass refineries (Swaminathan, 1994; Datta, 1995). As immunological methods, hybridoma technology, plant tissue and protoplast solved culture have many problems which could not be solved through conventional approach. Hence, DBT and CSB is giving more emphasis on bio-technological research in sericulture. Several research projects have been launched by above agencies by providing funds. Restriction fragment length polymorphism (RELP) Development of transgenic animals, analysis of genetic basis defence mechanism in silkworm, development of immunodiagnostic kit, semisynthetic diet for young and late age silkworm, mulberry improvement through biotechnology, biofertilizers *Azotobacter* and *Mycorrhiza*, sericultural pest management etc., are the important topic on which CSR and TI is conducting research in recent years. Datta (1995) says that convention and bio-technological approaches will help India to increase quality silk production in a big way, which will meet the increasing demand for both national and international markets. However, successful applications of bio-technology in the field of sericulture science and usher a new era of high silk production in tropics in near future (Datta, 1995; Dandin, 2002).

Attempts have been made for semisynthetic diet for young and late age silkworms and mulberry improvement through bio-technology under which tissue culture technique and mulberry screening of genotypes for adverse situation, quick multiplications of elite genotype, another culture and protoplast culture and fusion, etc. at CSR and TI, Mysore.

CSR and TI scientist made it possible to curtail 50% of recommended dose of chemical nitrogen fertilizer in mulberry cultivation through application of 20 kg. of Azotobacter biofertilizer without adversely affecting the leaf yield and quality (Das et al., 1992, 1993). It is also proved that by inoculating mulberry roots with vesicular arbuscular mycorrhizal fungi (VAM) to curtail the application of costly phosphoric fertilizer up to 75% of recommended dose of phosphoric fertilizer making mulberry cultivation much cheaper (Datta, 1995). However, in sericultural practices different concepts are adopted in India viz., low cost rearing houses (Fig. 37), low cost shoot feeding technique (Fig. 53, 54, 55), shoot feeding rearing by nylon shelved steel rack (Fig. 56, 57), traditional wooden tray rearing, etc. (Fig. 52)

CSR and TI, Mysore have made tremendous progress in controlling pests of mulberry like mealybug, *Maconellicoccus hirsutus* Green and Bihar hairy caterpillar, *Spilosoma obliqua* (Walk) by biological means. Many natural enemies belonging to Hymenoptera, Coleoptera, Neuroptera, Lepidoptera and Diptera are reported attacking the mealy bug. The predatory beetle, *Cryptolaemus montrouzieri* Muslant feed on stages of mulberry mealy bug. About 250 adults are required to be release per acre for controlling mealy bug on mulberry garden. Technology for large scale production of this beetle has been developed at CSR and TI, Mysore. Production cost of each beetle comes about 27 paise (Mani et al., 1987). The above institute is also practicing *Meteorus dichomeridis* for biological pest control of S. obliqu :. Recently, Sathe (2002) investigated intrinsic rates of increase and inferspecific compitation between two parastaid, *Meteorus dichomeridis* and M. spilosomae, the parastoids of Bihar hairy caterpillar S. obliqua for better implementation of biocontrol programme of S. obliqua.

Over 300 species of insect pests have been reported on mulberry from various parts of the world (Reddi and Kotikal, 1988) from Karnataka more than 100 insects pests have been reported (Manjunath et al., 1992). Recently, from Maharashtra more than

20 insect pests have been reported on mulberry (Sathe, 1998; Mulla, 1999; Sathe *et al.*, 1999; Sathe and Jadhav, 2001). In tropics loss of mulberry due to pest attack is estimated to be about 10% (Sengupta *et al.*, 1990). Mealy bug, *M. hirsutus* (Hemiptera, Peseudococcidae) known to be associated with mulberry for about 75 years in eastern India, has been recorded to inflict heavy damage in southern sericultural belt in recent years (Manjunath *et al.*, 1992).

Maharashtra is considered as a non traditional state of sericulture. Sericulture did not gain importance in Maharashtra due to alternate cash crops such as sugarcane, cotton, grapes etc. However, due to international demand to sericultural products, Maharashtra Government is taking keen interest in sericultural which resulted in submission of project to world bank of Rs. 37 crores recently. Sericulture in Maharashtra is not new. It is about four decades old.

Sericulture activities being practised on a limited scale in Maharashtra. A very few sections of the society are well acquainted with Tasar and Mulberry silk production. The state is yet to initiate organized efforts for exploring the possibility of Eri and Muga sericulture which has great potential in Western Maharashtra.

It has been observed that several attempts were made to introduce sericulture in Maharashtra during the 19th century as per earlier official records. Government officials come to know that sericulture trial project was initiated in 1827 but, ended by failure in the year 1847. Latter, efforts were also failed. However, Dr. G.P. Dewadikar, eminent botanist, agriculture scientist and cytogeneticist made a comprehensive attempts in around 1956-57. Mr. I.A. Kamte, successfully initiated the efforts at the time on his own to introduce sericulture in Maharashtra and achieved good success. Then few trails on a very small scale were undertaken which proved to be very successful and encouraging. Later, a broad based comprehensive sericultural programmes were conducted with an average success. However, the initial trials related to cultivation of various mulberry and non-mulberry food plants were initiated at panchgani, Mahabaleshwar and at the foot hills of Wai. However, the industry did not spread beyond borders of Wai till 1977-78 (Tayade, 1991). Later, this was followed by cultivating the selected mulberry varieties in different agroclimatic regions in

Maharashtra. Various varieties of mulberry and non-mulberry plants were cultivated on large scale for sericulture. The attempts were also made to the comparative trials of various species of mulberry and non-mulberry to asses their relative performance under local conditions and their acclimatization through selective breeding. Extension programmes were initiated based on these results which included formulation of a pattern which will be helpful to the various agriculturist. Thus, attempts were made with a view to maintain a supply of superior cutting of mulberry to the farmers of Maharashtra.

The initiative and favourable response by a few enterprising farmers, who had opportunities to be familiar with sericulture operations have introduced sericulture activity in the state on a modest scale. As a result, the state Government promoted sericulture in Maharashtra on large scale (Anonymous, 1998).

In the seventh five year plan the Government of Maharashtra made sincere efforts in promoting activity through Khadi and Village Industries Board which resulted, sericulture spread through out Maharashtra.

In Maharashtra Khadi and Village Industries Board was actively engaged in sericultural activities until recent years (1999). KVIB introduced few schemes under Western Ghat Development Plan (WEDP) and established pilot extension training centres (PETC), basic seed farm and grainage unit in Western Maharashtra. According to Tayade (1991) in 1990-91, 24 districts were engaged in sericultural practices and succeeded in establishing 5190 acres of mulberry plantation undertaken by 5879 farmers with production of 150 tons cocoons. But, sericultural activities increased after 1997. Sericulture programme was taken up at the instance of Government of Maharashtra for mulberry cultivation in 1,862 acres by 2000 farmers of 500 villages covering 75 talukas from 23 districts in all four regions of Maharashtra (Anonymous, 1998).

The sericulture programme was taken in 2665 acres by 2635 farmers of 975 villages from 24 districts in all four agroclimatic zones of Maharashtra during 1998-99. The mulberry cultivation area was about 10,000 acres in the year 1999-2000 in Maharashtra. During the years 2002-2003 the area under mulberry cultivation was more than 1500 acres.

Sericulture in Maharashtra has a tremendous potential, specially western Maharashtra has conducive environment for sericulture and secondly it is connected to Karnataka, sericulturally most advanced state of India. Vidharbha is famous for non mulberry sericulture in addition to mulberry sericulture.

Inspite of new strains and varieties of mulberry and silkworms released through biotechnology, the expected yield of the crop is not achieved so far because of mortalities in the worms due to natural enemies, pests and diseases etc. There are several natural enemies both from insect and non insect groups for silkworm *B. mori* (Sathe, 1998; Sathe and Jadhav, 2001). The insect natural enemies affect the cocoon production as they cause higher mortalities in the worms. The mulberry silkworms (*B. mori*) are attacked by uziflies, *Exorista bombycis* Louis, and *Exorista sorbillans* Wiedmann, *Xanthopimpla prdator* (Fabricius), *Apanteles glomeratus* Linn. (Sathe and Jadhav, 2001). *A. angaleti* Muesebeck, Dermestid bettles, praying mantids, etc. There are at least four species of uziflies viz., Japanese uzifly, *Crossocosmia sericariae* (Rondani), the lime uzifly, *Ctenophorocera pavida* (Meigen), the tasar uzifly, *Blepharipa zebina* Walker and the Indian uzifly, *E. Bombycis* associated with silkworms. (Tanaka, 1964; Jolly, 1967; Sathe and Jadhav, 2001).

According to Vender Wulp (1986) the Indian uzifly, *E. bombycis* is a primary parasitoid of the mulberry silkworm and distributed in British India, Assam, Bengal, Dehradun, Sri Lanka, Oriental region, Ethiopian and Palearctic regions (Beeson and Chatterjee, 1935). Japan (Ayuzawa *et al.*, 1972), Thailand (Ayuthaya, 1972) and Eastern Asia including West Bengal, Bihar and Assam in India extending up to Myanmar (Sri Haran *et al.*, 1971). The fly is very common in India, China, Thailand, South Korea and Myanmar. It is also reported from Canary Islands, Oriental region, South Palearetic and Afrotropical regions, New Guinea and Queensland (Krishnaswami *et al.*, 1973).

The uzifly was noticed for the first time in Ballanara Sapura village of Hoskote Tehsil at Bangalore district during May 1980 in Karnataka state (Anonymous, 1980). Earlier to this it was confined to North Eastern sericultural regions of the country, especially Bengal and Assam (Louis, 1980; Jameson, 1922). According to Rajshekargouda and Devaiahj (1983) it is well established in the five traditional silk producing districts viz., Bangalore, Kolar, Tumkur, Mysore and Mandya and has also spread to new areas of sericulture of the state. In some districts of Maharashtra, Sindudurg, Kolhapur, Sangli and Satara the Indian uzifly is well established.

The uzifly is known to cause 40 percent cocoon crop losses in some seasons in Eastern region of India (Anonymous, 1982). In Malda district of West Bengal during 1962-63, over 80 percent of cocoon production was lost due to uzi-infestation (Krishnaswami et al., 1964). In traditional states like Karnataka, Andhra Pradesh, Tamil Nadu overlapping nature of the silkworm rearings combined with the intensive movement of cocoon over long distances and negligence of the rearers initially to destroy the affected corps helped the spread of the pest throughout the states. Thus, several farmers lost the crop completely and continuously, 80 percent of the farmers rearings were reported to be affected by uzifly in certain parts of India. The cocoon yield per 100 dfls in Karnataka was reduced to as low as 5 to 10 kg (Anonymous, 1982). In Maharashtra 100% losses have been recorded in some fields of farmers and farms of State Government in the year 1996 (Jadhav, 1996).

The silkworm *Bombyx mori* has immense value in sericulture in India. It is domesticated easily as compared to other silkworms. However, *B. mori* is not disease free. Several diseases are associated with this worm. These diseases are caused by variety of agents like protozoa, fungi, bacteria, viruses, etc. The important diseases of silkworms are pebrine, flacherie, muscardine and grasserie. In India, 30-40% losses to the sericulture are recorded due to the diseases only but, Japanese have reduced the losses up to 10% (Devaiah, 1994). In India, successful efforts have been made to eliminate pebrine.

The pebrine was first reported from France in 1845. The pebrine is also called as peper disease or corpuscle disease, because of the black spots looking like pepper grain. Dequatrefages named the disease as "Peper disease" in 1860. However, the disease was not known in India up to 1895 (Janakiram, 1960).

In general, when silkworm is attacked by bacteria, the disease is called as "Flacherie". The flacherie cause very severe damage to silkworms under high humid conditions. Comparatively, flacherie cause more damage to silkworms than pebrine disease. It is believed that the pebrine is due to bad seeds and flacherie is the result of faulty rearing. In Karnataka, annual damage due to flacherie is about 20-40%. The term flacherie is used to describe the dysentries of silkworms.

The grasserie is caused by viral agent. It is called as "Jaundice" or nuclear polydedrosis. Jaundice is the name given to this disease because of the appearance of yellowish colour to affected worms and is quite appropriate.

The term muscardine is originated from the Italian word "moscardino" means lime like appearance or chalky. The muscardine disease is caused by fungi. The fungi lodged in the body of silkworm and penetrate in all directions by its network of blood sucking hyphae. Depending up on the etiology and colour of the spore, several types of muscardine of silkworms are visualized. Out of these, white muscardine, green muscardine and yellow muscardine and aspergillosis have greater importance.

No race is immuned completely to diseases (Jayaramaiah and Kuberappa, 1978) and different races of silkworm show variation in their susceptibility to different diseases (Liu Shixian, 1964). Preliminary work has been done on raring performance of different races of silkworm (Tikoo et al., 1971; Krishnaswami and Tikoo, 1971). Baig et al., (1998) screened 21 races of silkworm including pure and hybrid races for their relative susceptibility to Nuclear polyhedrosis under natural and induced conditions.

In past, researchers have been made to develop suitable method for the detection of disease at an early state of infection. Microbial diseases are diagnosed and identified by immunoassays. The assays are sensitive, specific and can be developed into simple immunodiagnostic kit to detect the infection even in crude samples.

At CSR and TI, Mysore and National Institute of Immunology, New Delhi, significant advances have been made under a DBT assisted research project towards development of immuno-diagnostic methods for detection of pebrine and viral diseases such as nuclear polyhedrosis and infectious flacherie (Dutta, 1995). In view of the inadequate disinfection and maintenance of unhygienic conditions in silkworm rearing areas, the use of disease tolerant silkworm breeds/hybrids can be a better option (Dandin, 2002). Many minor effect genes (Watanabe, 1986) control resistance of the silkworm to most of the pathogens. Therefore, breeding of tolerant strains to these pathogens is possible by selection of survivors after the exposure to the pathogen (Uzigawa and Aruga, 1966; Watanabe, 1967; Aratake, 1973). Adopting the same technology, CSR and TI, Mysore recently evolved a silkworm strain DR-1 which is resistant to BmNPV.

Indian sericulture was in a dormant condition till the advent of second world war. The progress of silk industry during the last fifteen years is remarkable. The cultural practices adopted for mulberry, selection of high yielding mulberry variety and leaves of good quality play a very important role for the successful harvest of cocoons. Further the maximum production of good quality cocoons also depends on the selection of silkworm variety. Univoltine and bivoltine silkworm varieties are known for the production of more quantity of better quality silk, when compared with multivoltines. There are different trends in rearing technology of silkworms (Krishnaswami, 1978; Ananthanarayana, 1986; Venugopalan Nayar, 1986; Mathur, 1988; Xiang et al., 1988; Mathur, 1991; Rajan et al., 1992 a, b., Inokuchi et al., 1993; Jadhav et al., 1998; Sathe et al., 1998; Jadhav et al., 2000a, b; Sathe and Jadhav, 2001a; Dandin, 2002; Mottaghitlab and Pourali, 2002; Ichida et al., 2002; and several other workers) including chauki rearing, late age rearing, leaf plucking method, shoot feeding method, Chinese rearing method, low cost rearing method, etc.

Rearing of silkworms is badly affected by abiotic and biotic factors. Several worker (Matsumara and Ishizuka, 1921; Veda and Lizuka, 1992; Sigematsu and Takeshita, 1967; Veda et al., 1969; Krishnaswami 1978 a, b, c; Krishnaswami et al., 1973; Anonymous, 1975; Hee, 1987; Das and Vijayaraghavan, 1990; Zhang et al., 2000; Huang et al., 2000; Muniraju et al., 2000; Jayaswal and Raut, 2000; Mathur et al., 2000; Gangwar et al., 2000; Naidu et al., 2001; Ramchandra et al., 2000; Katti et al., 2001; Radhakrishna et al., 2001; Jadhav et al., 2001; Saridiporn et al., 2002; Meechuen, 2002; Jadhav and Akare, 2002 etc.) contributed on rearing of silkworms with respect to biotic and abiotic factors. Among the abiotic factors, rearing temperature plays a vital role in the production potential of silkworms (Anonymous, 1975). Attempts have accordingly been

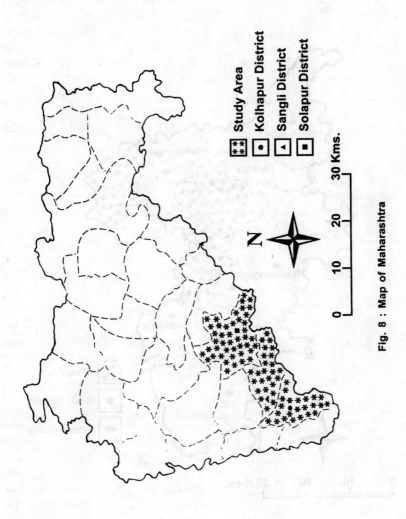

Fig. 8 : Map of Maharashtra

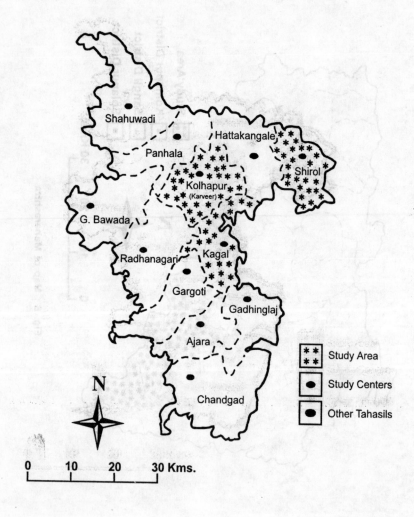

Fig. 9 : Map of Kolhapur District showing Study Area

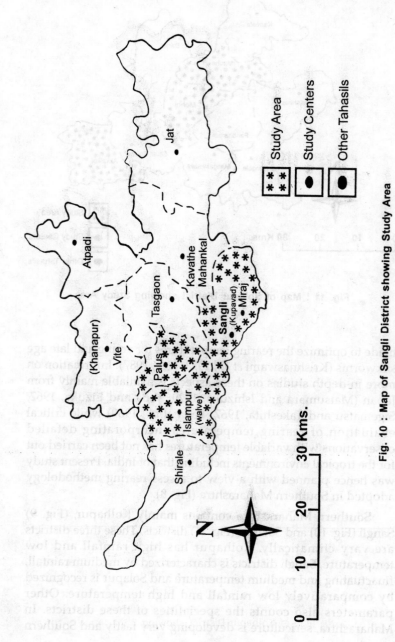

Fig. 10 : Map of Sangli District showing Study Area

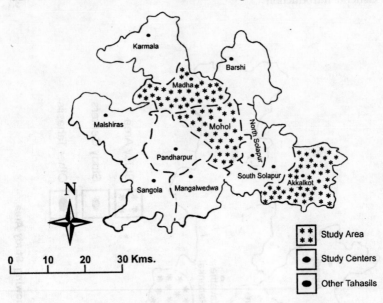

Fig. 11 : Map of Solapur District showing Study Area

made to optimize the rearing temperatures for young and late age silkworms (Krishnaswami *et al.*, 1973; Hee, 1987). Information on more in-depth studies on these aspects is available mainly from Japan (Matsumara and Ishizuka, 1929; Veda and Lizuka, 1962; Sigematsu and Takeshita, 1967; Veda *et al.*, 1969) while critical evaluation of rearing temperatures incorporating detailed observations with variable temperatures has not been carried out for the tropical environments including that of India. Present study was hence planned with a view to assess rearing methodology adopted in Southern Maharashtra (Fig. 8).

Southern Maharashtra contains mainly Kolhapur, (Fig. 9) Sangli (Fig. 10) and Solapur (Fig. 11) districts. These three districts are vary climatically. Kolhapur has high rainfall and low temperature, Sangli districts is characterized by medium rainfall, fluactuating and medium temperature and Solapur is recognized by comparatively low rainfall and high temperature. Other parameters also counts the specialities of these districts. In Maharashtra, sericulture is developing very fastly and Southern

Maharashtra is leading and play an important role in sericultural activities in Maharashtra. Keeping in view all above facts the present study was aimed to assess the rearing methodologies adopted in Southern Maharashtra with respect to abiotic and biotic factors. In past, no such type of study have been carried out in southern Maharashtra. However, Jadhav *et al.* (2000 a,b), Sathe and Jadhav (2001b), etc. have attempted the extension studies on sericulture in Southern Maharashtra.

2
REARING OF SILKWORMS

For any biological experimental work in the laboratory, it is necessary to maintain the culture of the experimental organism. Due to biotechnological advancement, modification/ulterations are possible for improving the rearing methods of insects. Sometimes very minor changes in techniques can have drastic results, both positive and negative. Application of wrong rearing technology results 100 percent losses in sericultural crops. Sericulture is technology oriented job and rearing of silkworms is soul of sericulture. The details of the materials and methods used for rearing mulberry silkworms are given below.

(A) REARING MATERIALS FOR *B. MORI.*

(1) *Rearing stand (Figs. 12, 20)*

Wooden rearing stand of the size 2.25 m in height, 1.5 m in length and 0.65 m in width consisting ten tiers were used for keeping rearing trays.

(2) *Ant wells (Fig. 13)*

Ant wells consist of enameled plate of 25 cm wide and 4 to 5 cm in depth and used for preventing ants in rearing bed.

(3) Rearing trays (Figs. 14, 21)

Rearing trays were made up of wooden material, of the size 3' long, 2' width and 6.5 cm depth (Fig. 14).

(4) Paraffin paper

Paraffin paper is a thick craft paper coated with paraffin was used for keeping the beds covered during rearing so as to prevent withering leaf and to maintain humidity.

(5) Foam rubber strips (Fig. 15)

Foam rubber strips of the size 2.5 cm x 2.5 cm thick, dipped in water were kept all round the silkworm bed in chawki rearing for maintaining humidity.

(6) Chopsticks

Chopsticks made of bamboo, about 17.6 cm to 22 cm long, thin in girth and tapering at the other end were used for picking delicate worms and preventing hygienic handling and damage to the worms.

(7) Lens (Fig. 16)

It was used for observing the silkworms.

(8) Feathers (Fig. 17)

Bird feather was used for brushing newly hatched worms and changing beds in the chawki rearing of silkworms.

(9) Chopping board and knife (Fig. 18,19)

The chopping board (Fig. 18) of soft wood with a size of 0.80 m x 0.80 m and thickness of 8.5 cm was used for chopping the leaves in early stage with blade size, 0.4 to 0.6 m long and 4 to 8 broad.

(10) Cleaning nets (Fig. 22)

The cotton nets were used for changing leaf over portion of mulberry leaves and litter of silkworms. Nets of different meshes to suit the stages of silkworm were used during rearing.

(11) Leaf basket

Leaf basket made up of bamboo were used for carrying the leaves from mulberry garden to rearing house and rearing the worms.

(12) Plastic leaf basket (Fig. 23)

(13) Mountages

(a) Chandrikes (Fig. 24)

Mountage composed of a rectangular bamboo mat on which was fixed a spiral of bamboo tape of the size 5' x 3' with 4 to 5 broad tape and the space between the spirals was 4 to 5 cm. Mountage was the contrivance used to enable the matured worms to spin cocoons.

(b) Plastic mountages (Fig. 25)

Nylon mountages made by CSR & TI, Mysore have been used for cocoon construction and easy harvesting.

(c) Local materials (Fig. 26 & 27)

Coconut dry fronds, red gram sticks, paddy sticks etc. were used for cocoon construction.

(14) Other appliances

A hygrometer (Fig. 28) of 'Barigo' company was used to ascertain temperature and humidity in rearing house (Fig. 36). A room heater (Fig. 29) was used to heat up the room for maintaining proper temperature. Disinfection pad, Sprayer (Fig. 30) and wash basin (Fig. 32) were used for disinfection and washing hands respectively with 2% formaldehyde solution.

(15) Vijetha powder (Fig. 31).

(16) Black boxing (Fig. 33).

(17) Water tank (Fig. 34).

(18) Leaf chamber (Fig. 35)

Leaf chamber was used for preservation of leaves in fresh condition. Leaf chamber made up of a framework of wooden strips 7.5 cm wide, spaced 7.5 cm on the sides and bottom, 130 cm × 70 cm high, covered on all sides with gunny cloth was kept wet to prevent the withering of mulberry leaves stored inside the chamber for rearing.

(19) Specimen tubes

The specimen tubes were used for keeping the parasitoid cocoons for adult emergence and handling the uzifly and other pest parasitoids. The open ends of tubes were covered with muslin cloth for good ventilation.

(20) Rearing rooms (Fig. 36, 37).

(21) Chawki rearing room (Fig. 44).

(22) Infrastructure of rearing room (Fig. 45).

REARING METHOD FOR *B. MORI.*

In the rearing farms, rearing of *B. mori* was started as per the method suggested by Jadhav *et al.* (2000).

The silkworm eggs (Fig. 38, 39) Pm x NB4D2 were brought from Government Silkworm Seed Production Centre. Incubation was done at room conditions (25±1°C, R.H. 75±3, 18:6 hr., L:D). Egg hatching period was 9-10 days. Newly hatched larvae were (Fig. 40) fed with tender mulberry leaves of M5 variety (Fig. 1) and brushed with feather into wooden rearing trays of the size 3'×2'. At the bottom and for covering of tray, paraffin papers were used so as to avoid humidity loss during chawki rearing. Low cost technique suggested by Jadhav *et al.* (2000) have adopted for late age rearing of silkworms. After and within the stage (instar) spacing and cleaning was performed for healthy growth of silkworms. There are five instars in the larval form. The 1st instar lasted for a period of 4 to 4.6 days, 2nd instar for 3 to 3.5 days, 3rd instar (Fig. 41) 3-4 days; 4th instars (Fig. 49) 4.6 days and 5th instar (Fig. 51) 7 to 8 days. The period required for larval development was 21-28 days. Full grown larvae (Fig. 42) were kept for spinning by using bamboo mountages (Fig. 25). Spinning lasted for 3-4 days. Harvested cocoons (Fig. 43) were kept for emergence in rearing of silkworms. Shoot feeding (Fig. 54) methods were adopted during the rearing of silkworms in selected farms of the farmers.

Ten farmers from each district (Kolhapur, Sangli and Solapur) with irrigation were selected for testing the rearing performance of mulberry silk worms *B. mori*, Pm x N_4D_2 with respect to biotic aboitic factors. All ten farmers in each district have performed shoot feeding method. Rearing performance of silkworms was assessed with respect to temperature, humidity, rainfall, light, diseases, pests and three different seasons viz., rainy, winter and summer. Other important conditions maintained during the rearing of silkworm by selected farmers are given below.

1.	Rearing methods adopted	Shoot feeding
2.	Mulberry variety used:	M-5
3.	Fertilizer dose	: N:P:K: 300 : 148:148 kg/ha/year in 5 splits. 30 mt farm yard manure per/ha/year in two splits
4.	Type of soil	Black
5.	Additional component applied to mulberry loans	No
6.	Rainfed/irrigated	Irrigated
7.	Chawki rearing	In trays
8.	Late age rearing	Low cost technique Indigenous shelves
	Silk worm spacing	
	a) 3rd instar	70 - 72 sq.ft.
	b) 4th instar	100 - 105 sq.ft.
	c) 5th instar	220 - 225 sq.ft.
9.	Disinfectants used Equipments used	Vijetha and Bleaching powder a) sprayer b) dusting pump c) cloth
10.	Montage used	Plastic mountage made by CSR & TI, Mysore.

Observations were also made on the rainfed rearing of silkworms adopted by another ten farmers in each three districts through questionnary for the assessment of rearing technique with respect to biotic and abiotic factors. The rearing of silkworms on rainfed crop have been assessed with the same parameter noted for irrigated crops.

In addition, a very large number of farmers have been consulted through questionnaire and their farms have been viewed from time to time for the assessment of rearing performance in Southern Maharashtra during the study period (2000-2002). Many farmers adopted different strategies and methods in their rearing farms (Figs. 44 to 48, 50, 53 and 59).

PLATE 3

Fig. 12 : Rearing stand with wooden trays; Fig. 13 : Ant Wells;
Fig. 14 : Rearing tray; Fig. 15 : Foam rubber strips;
Fig. 16 : Lens; Fig. 17 : Feathers

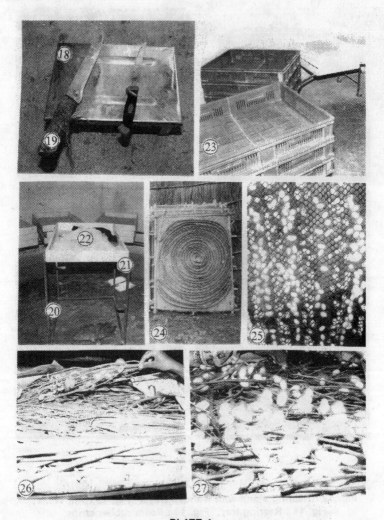

PLATE 4

Fig. 18 : Chopping board; Fig. 19 : Knife; Fig. 20 : Rearing stand;
Fig. 21 : Rearing tray; Fig. 22 : Cleaning net; Fig. 23 : Plastic leaf basket;
Fig. 24 : Chandrika; Fig. 25 : Plastic mountages;
Figs. 26-27 : Local Materials

PLATE 5

Fig. 28 : Hygrometer; Fig. 29 : Room heater; Fig. 30 : Sprayer;
Fig. 31 : Vijetha powder

PLATE 6

Fig. 32 : Wash basin; Fig. 33 : Black boxing; Fig. 34 : Water tank;
Fig. 35 : Leaf chamber

PLATE 7
Fig. 36 : Rearing room; Fig. 37 : Low cost rearing room

PLATE 8

Fig. 38 : Silkworms seed pocket; Fig. 39 : Silkworms eggs;
Fig. 40 : 1st instar silkworms (*B. mori*); Fig. 41 : 3rd instar silkworms;
Fig. 42 : 5th instar *B. mori*; Fig. 43 : Cocoons of *B. mori*

3
SHOOT FEEDING REARING METHOD
FOR SILKWORMS

Sericulture is an agrobased industry and labour requirement in agriculture is an acute problem now a days. Sericulture is laborious job. Labour input contributes more than 50% in silk worm rearing. Hence, reduction of labour requirement in the industry is burning problem, not only for rearing but also for reeling and fabrication.

The number of labour is not constant and confirm in rearing of silkworms. Hence, create problems for timely performance of the technique due to unavailability of labour as per our requirement. Adequate labour, time and sequence of activities, essentially counts the success of rearing towards increasing the profit margin. Therefore, labour is an important component of rearing technology. Saving the labour will add great relevance in obtaining maximum benefits to rearers.

Labour requirement is very less for chawki rearing and early instars. However, during last seven days, of rearing 50% of the total labour requirement is essential. Saving the labour in rearing of silkworms is an important trend in recent years and shoot feeding rearing is certainly helpful for decreasing the labour and cost of rearing of silkworms in late age. In Karnataka state, India, shoot rearing method is more famous than other states. In Kolar district of Karnataka this is traditional method visualized since last several decades. As compare to other crops such as sugarcane, cotton, tobacco etc. sericultural crop requires high labour. In every method of silk worm rearing, there is difference in rearing house pattern, equipments and mulberry plantation and cultivation. The adoption of shoot rearing method needs popularization amongst the farmers and various regions of India, as this is more economical and beneficial method.

Methods of silkworm rearing

1. Leaf picking method (Traditional method)
2. Shoot feeding method (Non-traditional method)

Leaf picking method

In leaf picking method individual leaves are picked/collected from mulberry garden and fed to the silk worms (*Bombyx mori* L.) in trays (Fig. 12) for cocoon formation. This method was commonly practised in India in previous decades. Leaf picking method is also called as traditional method of silkworm rearing. Leaf picking method requires high labour requirement in different stages of rearing viz. leaf picking, feeding, bed cleaning, etc. Hygiene has also relation with the type of rearing method. Leaf picking method can be adopted for all instars of the silk worm. This method is more laborious than shoot feeding method.

Shoot feeding method (Figs. 45-47, 54-58)

In shoot feeding method, rearing of silkworms is done by providing mulberry shoots (branches) instead of leaves as it preserves leaf quality for longer period during storage and on the bed better than leaf picking method. It can save labour about 70% than traditional method and there are several other advantages in this method. Now a days, in India sericulturists are giving more emphasis on shoot feeding method than leaf picking method of silk worm rearing. However, in Japan and China sericulturally advanced countries, shoot rearing is very common practice since last several years. In the countries mentioned above this method is adopted throughout the year.

Requirements of shoot feeding

1. Mulberry garden
2. Rearing house

3.   Rearing appliances

4.   Disinfectants etc.

Mulberry garden

Irrigated mulberry garden is to be developed for shoot feeding rearing method of silkworms. 45 day old mulberry shoots (branches) are normally used in the shoot feeding method. But, may have little alteration with respect to soil, season, varieties etc. Non irrigated mulberry is not suitable for shoot feeding. Irrigated mulberry with row (Fig. 5) or pit system of plantation are recommended by sericultural institutes. During a year irrigated crop can be harvested for 6-7 times with high potential of cocoon production quantity and quality. The distance between two plants should be 6" to 9" and the distance between two rows should be 9" to 12". After first crop (harvestation of branches), it can be harvested after 45 days. Fertilizers and composting doses for mulberry are same as recommended for traditional rearing method. However, fertilizer doses are little bit dependent on quality of soil. Irrigation time and type are also similar to traditional method.

Rearing House

Rearing house should be nearer to mulberry garden and below the shade of trees or surrounded by shady trees. Standard size and description of rearing house for shoot feeding is given by Sekharappa *et al.*, (1997). However, as a low cost technique, simple thatched roof or shade (Fig. 37) may be preferred. The shoot feeding rearing can be started in simple thatched hut/thatched roof of size 32' long and 16' wide. The maximum height of thatched roof is 14'-15' at the centre while, at sides it is 4'-5'. The side walls are prepared with bajra or sorghum kadbbi/Tur (pigeon pea) straw. For better ventilation windows are designed at the distance of 5' on all the side walls of roof. The windo-shutters may be prepared by using card board material of waste packings. The roof may be prepared with the help of locally available wood, bajra/sorghum kadbbi, dry grasses, dry sugarcane leaves, etc. In each roof two rearing racks are prepared as described above.

Expenditure on 200 dfls of silkworm

1. 200 dfls ... Rs. 300

2. i) Young silkworm rearing - 12 days ... 1 Man per day-
   12 men days

   ii) Late age silkworm rearing 12 days,
   1 man per day, 12 men days

   iii) Spreading of silkworm on mountages
   and harvesting of cocoons ... 2 days, 3 men-
   6 men days

   Total ... 900 = 00

3. Parafin paper, Formalin, R.K.O., ... 150 = 00
   News papers, etc.

4. **Expenditure on first year**

   1. Wages for primary expenditure ... 200.00

   2. Mulberry plantation, wages,
      equipments, others ... 5500.00

   3. Annual expenditure equipments for
      silkworm rearing ... 1000.00

   4. Rearing shed/rearing house
      (share of first year) ... 1000.00

   5. Rearing house construction ... 1000.00

      8700.00

   6. First year's total expenditure
      on 600 dfls (3 crops) ... 4000.00

      Total ... 12700.00

Expenditure for second year

Similar investment is visualized for second year except the additional expenditure occurred on additional dfls taken. In second year 1200 dfls can be brushed with 6 crops. Additional investment for second year is about Rs. 4000 to 4500. Thus, total expenditure comes about 12700 + 4500 = 16200.

Table 1 : Rearing requirement for shoot feeding system in standard method

Sr. No.	Item	Unit cost (Rs.)	Life in years	Cost per year	Two acres (300 dfls/brushing)		
					Quantity	Total cost	Cost/Year
1.	Wooden chawki rearing tray 4' × 3' × 2½"	200	10	20.00	24	4,800	480.00
2.	Chawki bottom stand	250	10	25.00	2	500	50.00
3.	Rearing stand for 3rd stage worms 12 tires	1200	10	120.00	2	2400	240.00
4.	Feeding Stand	200	10	20.00	1	200	20.00
5.	Ant Wells	20	10	2.00	48	960	96.00
6.	Leaf Chamber (4' × 2.5' × 2.5')	850	10	85.00	1	850	85.00
7.	Shoot rearing rack 3 tires unit 5' × 35'	2500	10	225	2	5000	500.00
8.	Bed Cleaning net	15	5	3.00	24	360	72.00
9.	Bamboo Mountages 4' × 6'	200	5	40.00	90	18,000	3600.00
10.	Sprayer	1750	10	175	1	1750	175.00
11.	Gas Mask	1200	10	120	1	1200	120.00
12.	Wet and Dry Thermometer	200	10	20.00	2	400	40.00
13.	Room heater and Thermostat	750	5	150.00	1	750	150.00
14.	Plastic basins (Big + Small)	50 + 35	3 3	17.00 12.00	2 2	100 70	33.50 23.50
15.	Plastic bucket Big Small (10 Ltr.)	60 45	3 3	30.00 15.00	2 2	120 90	40.00 30.00

Contd...

Table 1 – Contd...

Sr. No.	Item	Unit cost (Rs.)	Life in years	Cost per year	Two acres (300 dfls/brushing) Quantity	Total cost	Cost/Year
16.	Foam pad 2" × 2" (1 Kg)	300	5	60.00	1.5	450	90.00
17.	Forceps	50	10	5.00	2	100	10.00
18.	Plastic Seave	45	3	15.00	1	45	15.00
19.	Foot mat	60	1	60.00	3	180	180.00
20.	Plastic Mug	30	3	10.00	2	60	20.00
21.	Leaf Chopping Board	150	10	15.00	1	150	15.00
22.	Leaf Chopping Knife	100	3	33.50	2	200	20.00
23.	Rearing Building (Shoot Storing room)	200/ Sq. Ft.	20	10.00	1148	2,29,600	11,480.00
	Total						**2,68,335**

* Rs. 15,000 per 100 Sq. ft. for low cost house, Rs. 45,000 per Sq. ft for R.C.C. roof.

Other items and rate Flexibility error. 50,000

    Grant Total   50,000 + 2,68,335 = Rs. 3,18,335.00

Expected income

1. For the first year from 600 dfls. 210 kg.
   cocoons at the rate of 136/kg.   28,770.00

2. For the second year from 1200 dfls.
   420 kg. cocoon at the rate of 136/kg.   57,540.00

Net benefit

For Ist Year   28,770 - 12,700 =   16,070.00

For IInd Year   57,540 - 16,200 =   41,340.00*

---

* Expected annual net benefit after 1st year for several years. Even it is expected more than this account too.

The cost required for shoot feeding method of 'silkworm rearing' under low cost technique is shown below :

Table 2 : Expenditure and material required for low cost shoot feeding method

Sr. No.	Item	Total Cost (in Rs.)	Age of item	Cost of item/year (in Rs.)
1.	Silkworm Rearing shed/ thatched roof silkworm rearing house	15000-27000	20	750-1000
2.	Nylon net (2 bundles)	1200	10	120.00
3.	Bamboo for stand	500	5	100.00
4.	Wooden trays (20) 3' × 2' × 2½"	2000	10	200.00
5.	Leaf knife - (2)	200	5	40.00
6.	Leaf chamber (1)	400	10	40.00
7.	Leaf chopping board (1)	150	10	15.00
8.	Sprayer pump (1)	1750	10	175.0
9.	Hydrometer (1)	150	10	15.00
10.	Foam pad (1 kg)	300	5	6000
11.	Mountages (50)	9000	5	1800
	Total	35,650.00		3,565.00

Rearing methods of shoot feeding

1. *Kolar method*

This method is adopted as a traditional method of silkworm rearing by providing shoots to worms in Kolar district of Karanataka State. Hence, this method is called as Kolar method. This is quite popular and provided good results in Karanataka.

Special features of this method

i)   **Mulberry plantation** - has great importance. Distance between two plants is 6" to 9" and the distance between two rows is 9" to 12". Second crop can be harvested after 45 days of first crop.

ii) **Trays** (Figs. 50-51) - are rounded and made up of bamboo and plastered by cowdung. **Size** - 3.5' to 4' diameter, 2" to 2.5" in height.

iii) 20 trays are required for 100 dfls.

iv) Size of mountage - 6' x 4' and

v)   Bamboo tripe is 125' to 150 long, distance between two strips is 1.5 inch.

Uses of leaves

Shoot leaves are provided to silkworm by cutting shoots from the base. The entire shoot branch is given to worms in first case. This material is given to silkworms upto the formation of cocoons. In second case, growing shoots or tender leaves cut into small pieces are given to silkworms of young age specially for first three instars. But, for third instars and onwards the entire branch (shoot) is cut from the base and given to the worms. Some times, when mulberry grows for more than 2', then the mulberry branches of 6" to 8" length may be given to the silkworm by cutting from the plants. It is advisable that after each crop all equipments and rearing room/roof/shed should be sterilized by disinfectants.

2. Second method of shoot feeding

In this case instead of bamboo trays, strips of nylon net are used. The width of the nylon net strips is ranged from 3' to 5' while, length varies from 60' to 80' depending upon size of rearing house/rearing roof/ shed. The distance between two strips is 1.5' to 2'. Here, the rack is prepared with the help of sticks of bamboo. In addition common rearing house of size 120'x60' made up of cement concrete can also be used.

3. Third method of shoot feeding

Longer racks of nylon net/cloths are used in this method. Rack arrangement is of the size, 5' wide x 35' long. It also shows 6" edge to prevent falling of worms from the rack. On such bed 20,000 worms or 50 dfls worms can be grown upto cocoon stage by providing mulberry branches. These branches are arranged in such a way that top of one branch can match the base of another. The rack may have 2-3 tiers of 26" to 30" distance. The racks are made up of bamboo, wood or iron (Figs. 45-48, 54, 55). In this case rearing house is of length 40' to 60' or 120' made up of cement concrete. The rearing house may contain large windows for ventilation. However, chawki rearing room is of size, 10'x10'. For cocoon construction, bamboo made Chandriki or mountages are used. It is better to keep all chandriki in a separate room for uniform cocoon development and proper harvestation of cocoons. The special feature of this method is the mulberry cultivation by keeping 2'x2' or 3'x3' distance between two mulberry plants.

Fourth method of shoot feeding

The mulberry garden of first year is generally not used for shoot feeding method. Because, during the first year, the root system of plant is to be established deep in soil. Once it is established, then garden is ready for the use for shoot feeding. After one year, plant will not affect after cutting the branches and also the yield of shoots. Shoot cutting before one year may affect the number of mulberry plants and quantity of leaves. The branches of mulberry are cut-down from 1.5' to 2' height from ground level for the safety of plants. However, the plant should be sufficiently grown, of diameter of arm when it is cut-down for shoot feeding. During a year 5-6 crops can be harvested by leaf stage and by shoot branch. Mulberry cultivation of 2'x2' plantation is beneficial for this method. Within 45 days after 1st crop harvest, second crop is taken. Irrigated land is the prerequisite for this method.

Fifth method of shoot feeding

Mulberry cultivation plays an important role in this method. Mulberry is cultivated by sari (row) type method. In this method, sari is of 2' or 3' wide (Fig. 7). The distance between two saries is 5 feet. Mulberry is planted to both sides of sari after 1 feet distance between the two plants. The plant number is comparatively more than other type of mulberry cultivation, it comes about 10,000 or more. Water is sufficiently saved by this method. Likely, mixed cropping is also possible. This method is visualized as most economic method from the view point of benefits to farmers.

Fertilizers

20 Bullock cars per acre are recommended as organic or Drug composting to mulberry garden. However, there is no limit for dung cow fertilizer. It is always beneficial to mulberry plants. Dung is burried in between two rows of mulberry and then the garden is drop irrigated. This is most useful to the garden. For increase in yield biofertilizers and other fertilizers are also recommended. Chemical fertilizers are recommended as 1 bag of mixed fertilizer (N:P:K) 19:19:19 or 15:15:15 and 1/2 bag of urea. Irrigation is essential after fertilizer dose. It is advised that after harvest of 1st crop, ploughing is done by bullock anchor or baliram anchor. Thus, the soil is exposed to sun for 4-5 days and then fertilizer is applied. Biofertilizers are also used to increase the yield of crop. It is applied in the form of Sunhemp, Ghencha, Velu, etc.

Chawki rearing of silkworms

Chawki rearing refers to the rearing of 1st to 3rd instars of silkworm. Chawki rearing period lasts for 7 to 12 days. During this period temperature should be 27-28°C and humidity (R. H.) should range 80-90%. The worms need highly nutritive and tender leaves. During chawki rearing about 4 to 5% of the total requirement of leaves is needed. 45 to 50 kg leaves are sufficient to rear 100 dfls and only one man is sufficient for doing the formalities of chawki rearing. Chawki rearing room is shown in Fig. 44.

Initiation of rearing

Layings should be taken in wooden try of size 4'x3'2.5" from black box (Fig. 33) and exposed to morning light between 7 a.m. to

8 a.m. for uniform hatching of the larvae. Uniform hatching, growth and cocoon construction are crucial factors for success of sericulture business. Newly hatched larvae should be fed with fresh tender leaves by cutting into pieces of size 0.25 Cm^2 with the help of knife. Larvae should be transferred on wax paper after 1-2 hrs. of initial feeding through egg cards. The rearing bed should be of size 4 sq. ft. To maintain proper humidity, foam pads (Fig. 15) should be arranged around the bed and covered by parafin wax paper. For proper rearing of worms the information given in Table -3 should be followed. The Table-3 provides information about size of the bed, quantity of leaves, bed cleaning, feeding time etc.

Late age rearing

3rd to 5th instar larvae of *Bombyx mori* L. are reared under late age rearing. These worms require less temperature (24-26°C) and humidity (70-75%) as compared to young worms (chawki rearing). Likely, these worms require sufficient and good quality shoots. Good quality branches (shoots) should be 55 to 60 day old. (after planting or 1st cutting). 4th instar requires about 12.5 % of the total quantity of leaves for rearing of silk worm, while 5th instar needs 82% of the total. Ariation has a very significant role in late age rearing. Good ariation always prevent diseases of silk worm.

A single man can collect 150 kg mulberry branches (shoots) during a day. Branches should be carried out with bundles. Each bundle may contain 30 to 40 kg of mulberry shoots. The bundles of branches should be kept inverted (bottom at base) in a less ventilated room. To maintain freshness of leaves quadrangle on ground is prepared and about 2" water is pored on it. The length of a branch should be dependant to the rack of rearing house. A five feet rack will be required for 3 to 4 feet long mulberry branches for easy matching and preparing bed. At the time of harvestation, the average height of the plants should be 3 to 4 ft. Branches should be harvested at morning and evening (at cool period).

Feeding

When silkworms shed their cuticle 3rd time, they should be taken on rack of nylon net (Method-2/Method-3). The rearing house/ shed/roof, and entire equipments used in rearing should be disinfected with disinfectants. On the nylon net arrange news

Table 3 : Chawki rearing requirements for 100 dfls. (CB)

Stage of larvae and room condition	Age in days	Feeding time	Leaf size in sq.cm.	Leaf quantity in gms.	Bed area sq. ft.	Remarks
Ist instar 27-28°C 85-90% RH	1	10.00 AM	0.5 × 0.5	500	4.00	Expose layings to morning light from 7-8 AM. Brush larvae around 9 AM. Make bed after 30 min. and give feeding.
		4.00 AM	0.5 × 0.5	500	4.00	
		10.00 PM	0.5 × 0.5	500	7.5	
	2	5.00 AM	1.0 × 1.0	1,300	7.5	Spread the bed half an hour before feeding for drying.
		10.00 AM	1.0 × 1.0	1,300	7.5	
		4.00 PM	1.5 × 1.5	1,300	7.5	
		10.00 PM	1.5 × 1.5	1,300	10.5	
	3	5.00 AM	1.5 × 1.5	1,200	10.5	Bed spreading half an hour, then feeding. Bed cleaning by net, observe moulting behaviour. After symptoms reduce leaf size and quantity.
		10.00 AM	1.5 × 1.5	1,200	10.5	
		4.00 PM	1.5 × 1.5	1,200	15.0	
		10.00 PM	0.5 × 0.5	1,200	15.0	
Ist moult 27-28°C, 75% RH	4	6.00 AM	0.5 × 0.5	200	15.0	Give light feeding. After settlement of 90% of moulting larvae, stop feeding. Break/spread the bed. Apply lime powder to dry the bed.
		10.00 AM	0.5 × 0.5	200	15.0	
		4.00 PM	0.5 × 0.5	200	15.0	
		10.00 PM	0.5 × 0.5	200	15.0	
IInd instar 27-27°C 75% R.H.	5	5.00 AM	1.5 × 1.5	3,500	15.00	Give feeding after 90% of the larvae found moulted. Disinfect bed before feeding, clean bed.
		10.00 AM	1.5 × 1.5	3,500	15.00	
		4.00 PM	1.5 × 1.5	3,500	15.00	
		10.00 PM	2 × 2	3,500	30.00	
	6	5.00 AM	2 × 2	4,250	30.00	Spreading of bed for ½ hr. before feeding. Apply Disinfectant to dry bed.
		10.00 AM	2 × 2	4,250	30.00	
		4.00 PM	2 × 2	4,250	30.00	
		10.00 PM	2 × 2	4,250	45.00	

Contd...

Table 3 – Contd...

Stage of larvae and room condition	Age in days	Feeding time	Leaf size in sq.cm.	Leaf quantity in gms.	Bed area sq. ft.	Remarks
	7	5.00 AM	2 × 2			Observe moulting, reduce leaf size and quantity of food, clean the bed before settlement of larvae for moult.
		10.00 AM	1 × 1	11,00	45.00	
IInd moult 26-27°C 75% R.H.	8	4.00 AM				Stop feeding if observed 90% of larvae settled for moult. Break/spread bed. Apply lime powder. Keep bed dry.
		10.00 PM				
		5.00 AM				
		10.00 AM		45.00		
	9	4.00 AM	2 × 2	3,000	45.00	Disinfect larvae/bed if 90% larvae moults, give feeding, clean bed, give feeding after drying and cleaning bed.
		10.00 PM	3 × 3		45.00	
		5.00 AM	3 × 3			
		10.00 AM	3 × 3	9,000	60.00	
		4.00 PM	3 × 3			
		10.00 PM	4 × 4			
IIIrd Instar 25-26°C 75-90% R.H.	10	5.00 AM	4 × 4	12,000	60.00	Spread the bed before every feeding for drying. Clean the bed and give feeding.
		10.00 AM	4 × 4	12,000		
		4.00 PM	4 × 4	12,000		
		10.00 PM	4 × 4	12,000		
	11	5.00 AM	4 × 4		90.00	Clean the bed.
		10.00 AM	4 × 4	8,000	90.00	
		4.00 PM	2 × 2			Observe moulting behaviour, reduce leaf size and leaf quantity
		10.00 PM	2 × 2			
IIIrd moult 25°C 75% R.H.	12	5.00 AM			90.00	Stop feeding after settlement of 90% of the larvae for moult. Break/spread the bed. Apply lime powder. Dry the bed.
		10.00 AM				
		4.00 PM				
		10.00 PM			90.00	

papers and prepare bed by using mulberry branches (shoots). The top and bottom ends of branches should be placed alternatively for providing all types of leaves to worms (Fig. 56) Beds are examined for screening diseased worms. The diseased worms should be dipped in to 2% formalin or lime solution and then disposed for avoiding future infestation. In wet season and due to low temperature and excess feeding, the bed becomes wet. This is dried with the help of dusting lime powder. The feeding time is delayed if more leaves found on the bed.

Spacing

For 100 dfls, 300 to 350 sq. ft. space is essential. Worms may be transferred along with mulberry branches and uniform spacing is made on bed. 100-115 silkworms are expected in 1 sq.ft. area. Bed area, feeding time and other details are given in Table-4.

Care during Moult

Larvae shed their cuticle only once during the late age rearing of shoot feeding method. This moult is the 4th moult of the worms. A group of 90% of the larvae settles for moult during which they stop feeding. Then a disinfectant, lime powder is dusted uniformly and bed is kept dried. Stop giving feed to larvae during moulting. After 8 hrs the bed should be examined with respect to non moulting (non settling) and diseased larvae. The diseased larvae should be disposed/killed after disinfecting them with 2% formalin solution so that they would not be the source of future reinfestation. The non-moulted worms should be collected and reared separately by providing branches once or twice. Because, uniform and timely cocoon formation is essential for uniform harvestation of cocoons and marketing. Low humidity and ariation are the important components of rearing of late age silkworms.

Bed cleaning

In traditional method bed cleaning is done everyday in 4t¹ and 5th instars. However, in shoot feeding method, bed cleaniṛ is done only once i.e. on the 2nd day of 5th instar. The leave associated with mulberry branch are consumed by larvae at good condition. Hence, only branched stricks are left behind and they can be collected. Bed cleaning is done by two methods viz., Rope method and Net method.

Table 4 : Late age shoot feeding : feeding time, bed size and other details

Instars	Age in days	Feeding time	Quantity of food fed (kgs.)	Bed Area feet	Remarks
4th instar	1	8.00 AM	6	5 × 15	After 3rd cuticle sheding larvae may be shifted to rack and fed with mulberry branches.
		3.00 PM	8	5 × 15	
		10.00 PM	10	5 × 15	
	2	8.00 AM	12	5 × 20	Increase the bed before feeding.
		3.00 PM	15	5 × 20	
		10.00 PM	17	5 × 20	
	3	8.00 AM	19	5 × 30	Increase the bed before feeding.
		3.00 PM	22	5 × 30	
		10.00 PM	24	5 × 30	
	4	8.00 AM	22	5 × 30	Bed should be dried, examine features of moulting behaviour of larvae, accordingly feeding may be decreased.
		3.00 PM	20	5 × 30	
		10.00 PM	18	5 × 30	
		8.00 AM	8	5 × 30	
4th moulting stage	1	3.00 PM	–	5 × 30	Ensure that 90% of the total larvae are setting for moult, then stop feeding and then disinfect the bed with bleaching powder.
		10.00 PM	–	5 × 30	
		8.00 AM	–	5 × 30	
		3.00 PM	–	5 × 30	
5th instar	1	10.00 PM	16	5 × 30	After moulting of 90% larvae give dusting of RKO, then give feeding. Bed is cleaned after 2-3 feeding.
		8.00 AM	19	5 × 30	
		3.00 PM	22	5 × 30	
		10.00 PM	26	5 × 30	
	2	8.00 AM	30	5 × 35	Increase bed and give feeding.
		3.00 PM	34	5 × 35	

Contd...

Table 4 – Contd...

Instarts	Age in days	Feeding time	Quantity of food fed (kgs.)	Bed Area feet	Remarks
	3	10.00 PM	38	5 × 35	
		8.00 AM	42	5 × 55	Expand bed, dust RKO before feeding.
		3.00 PM	46	5 × 55	
		10.00 PM	48	5 × 55	
	4	8.00 AM	50	5 × 60	Increase bed, see health of larvae.
		3.00 PM	54	5 × 60	
		10.00 PM	60	5 × 60	
	5	8.00 AM	62	5 × 70	Expand bed, disinfect bed with RKO and give normal feeding.
		3.00 PM	66	5 × 70	
		10.00 PM	72	5 × 70	
	6	8.00 AM	76	5 × 70	Expand bed, disinfect bed with RKO and give normal feeding.
		3.00 PM	78	5 × 70	
		10.00 PM	80	5 × 70	
	7	8.00 AM	82	5 × 70	Give normal feeding and disinfect bed.
		3.00 PM	82	5 × 70	
		10.00 PM	70	5 × 70	
	8	8.00 AM	65	5 × 70	Observe spinning behaviour and mount spinning larvae on the mountage at the rate of 50/sp.ft.
		3.00 PM	50	5 × 70	
		10.00 PM	40	5 × 70	
		8.00 AM	10	5 × 70	

For bivolline breeds - 10% more feed is required. The above chart is for multivoline

Rope method

In this method, two ropes longer than the bed size or 6 feet in length are spread parallel on bed by leaving 1.5 feet area on both side. Then provide mulberry branches 2 to 3 times to worms on the ropes. Next day before offering shoots, branches are rolled inwardly with the help of ropes. Then mulberry sticks are removed. Likely, worms are also removed with branches. Other waste material along with news papers are removed from the bed. After removing the old bed new branches are spread leaving the ropes below the bed. Thus, ropes are helpful for removing the bed at the end of rearing.

Net method

Cotton net of size 5x6 feet with 2x2 cm holes are used in this method for cleaning the bed. The net is spread over bed. Then 2-3 feedings are given to worms on the net, the net is then removed/ lifted and the old bed is cleaned. On the net bed is prepared for worms. After making the bed, the bed is disinfected with RKO at 7-8 gms per sq.ft.

Spinning

On 7th or 8th day the 5th instar larvae start feeding less, shrink in size, becomes yellow and start wandering in the bed with raised head. Feeding quantity should be reduced (Table-4) by observing the above characteristics in the larvae. Lime powder is uniformly applied to bed when moulting larvae observed - feeding the larvae with chopped shoots (3"-4" long) reduces the cocoon formation time in bed. The spinning larvae should be identified immediately and picked out from the bed by hand and put on mountages for cocoon formation. The larvae may be managed on the mountage at the rate of 50-60 worms per sq. ft. Harvestation of cocoon is done after 5th day of spinning in summer and 6th day in winter. Cocoons are loosely filled in the bags, at the rate of 20-30 kg/bag during transportation.

Advantages of Shoot rearing

1. Leaves does not go waste. Leaf saving is upto 15-25%. Leaves dry slowly than leaf feeding method. Hence, larvae feed more and produce good quality cocoons.

2. Entire leaves (100%) are utilized for feeding by silk worms as some leaves get dried and drop down in leaf cutting method.

3. Maximum worms are reared (1.5 times more than traditional method).

4. Reduces labour requirement hence, more economic (it reduces 50-70% labour than traditional method).

5. Handling of worms is minimized.

6. Provides better ariation to worms.

7. Secondary contamination is minimized.

8. Many other benefits.

Disadvantages

1. Requires more (+ 30%) rearing room floor area.

2. No bed refusal left for cattle.

3. Planting material is lost.

4. Needs more attention for disinfection.

PLATE 9

Fig. 44 : Chawki rearing room; Fig. 45 : Infrastructure of rearing room
(Advance iron rearing house)

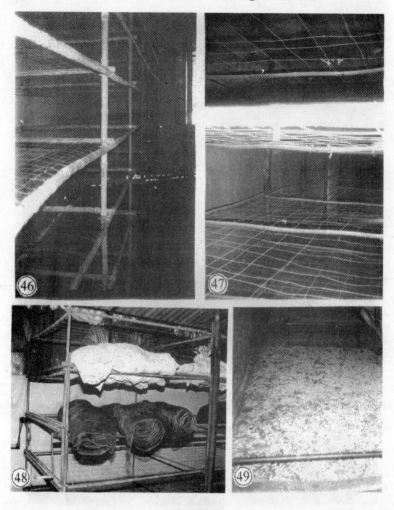

PLATE 10

Fig. 46 : Bomboo rearing device; Fig. 47 : Rearing device made up of
wood and iron wire gage; Fig 48 : Rearing rack with nylon net
(stored); Fig. 49 : Silkworm larvae (4th instar)

PLATE 11

Fig. 50 : Traditional rearing of silkworm with bamboo baskets;
Fig. 51 : Bamboo basket with silkworms (5th instar);
Fig. 52 : Wooden rearing cabinet (Traditional method);
Fig. 53 : Low cost indigenous saree shelf

PLATE 12

Fig. 54 : Low cost rearing trend (shoot feeding);
Fig. 55 : Low cost rearing trend

PLATE 13

Fig. 56 : Advanced silkworms rearing with iron shelves;
Fig. 57 : Advanced rearing with mobile iron shelves

PLATE 14

**Fig. 58 : Author with government officials, Department of Sericulture
Govt. of Maharashtra; Fig. 59 : Mountages with local material
(coconut fronds and mulberry sticks)**

4
ECOLOGICAL ASPECTS OF REARING

Ecological aspects of rearing silkworm (*B. mori*) in Southern Maharashtra, India have been discussed in the chapter. Kolhapur (Fig. 9) district is located between 15° to 17° North latitude and 73° to 74° East longitude. The district is bounded by Sangli district at the North, Belgaun district of Karnataka State at the South and East and Ratnagiri and Sindhudarga district at the West. The area of the district is 7633 sq. km. Its population is more than 20,03,953. The district contain 12 tahsils.

The main part of the district is traversed by the Sahyadry mountains in the West. It has thrown several spur's in the East of the district. Major portion of the district is 390 to 600 metres above mean sea level. The principal rivers of Kolhapur district are the Krishna, the Warna, the Panchganga, the Doodhganga, the Vedganga and the HiranyKeshi. The Warna river, which has fairly South Eastern trend, serves as the boundry between Kolhapur and Sangli district. The Panchanganga is formed by the four tributaries namely, the Kasari, the Kumbhi, the Tulashi and the Bhogawati. The Panchanganga falls into the Krishna at Narsobawadi in Shirol tahsil. The South Western region of the district is drained by the Doodhaganga river.

The forests in Kolhapur district are confined to the Western half of the district. The total forest area in Kolhapur district is more than 1,46,575 hectares (Annonymous, 1982). With respect to soil,

Kolhapur district has three broad zones, the Western part is covered with lateritious soil, the Central part has fertile, brownish, well drained soil while, the Eastern zone is covered with alluvial medium the deep black soil.

The rainfall is not evenly distributed in the district and it varies from place to place. Bavada in the West receives a little over 6000 mm rainfall while, Hatkanangle in the East receives rainfall as little as 500 mm. The district gets rain from the South West as well as from the South East monsoon. The main rainy season is from June to October.

Ajra, Chandgad, Bavada, Radhanagari and Shahuwadi tahsils come in the heavy rainfall tract. In this tract the normal rainfall ranges from 2096 mm, in Chandgad tahsil to 6232 mm in Bavada tahsil. Bhudargad, Gadhinglaj and Karvir tahsils have sufficient rainfall, while Kagal tahsil falls in inadequate rainfall tract. The remaining two tahsils viz. Hatkanangle and Shirol tahsils may be classified under poor rainfall tract. The normal rainfall in both these tahsils is less than 600 mm. The Kolhapur district is well known for sugarcane production.

Sangli district (Fig. 10) is one of the part of the famous "Deccan Plateau". It lies between 16° 45' "and 17° 38' North latitudes and 73° 42' and 75° 40' East longitudes. This district is bounded on East by Bijapur district of Karnataka state. On the West by Ratnagiri on the South by Kolhapur (MS) and Belgaum district of Karnataka state. The districts Satara and Solapur lies on the North boundries of this district. This district falls partly in Krishna basin and partly in Bhima basin. Consequently, it is divided into different drain systems. The whole district can also be divided into three different parts on the basis of topography, climate and rainfall-

1. Western hilly area of Shirala tahsil with heavy rainfall.

2. The basin area of Krishna, Warna and Yerala comprising of Walwa tahsil, Eastern part of Shirala tahsil, Western parts of Miraj and Tasgaon tahsils.

3. Eastern drought prone areas which comprises Eastern part of Miraj and Tasgaon tahsils, North Eastern part of Khanapur and whole of Atpadi, Kavathe mahankal and Jath tahsils. There are two main systems of hills, 1) Sahyadri ranges and its offshoots, 2) Offshoots of

Mahimangad Panhala ranges. Krishna, with its Warna and Yerala tributaries, flows through the Western part of the district. Agrani, Man and Bor rivers constitute the drain system for the eastern part of the district. The water resources from these rivers are very limited and these rivers remain dry for the major part of the year. The soils of varied texture and structure are observed in Sangli district. 1) The soil in the Western part of the district, comprising area from Shirala tahsil, it formed from red laterite mixed with hard-murum due to the hilly nature of the zone. This type of soil contains iron compounds and has a good property of drainage. 2) The central portion of the district which covers areas of Walwa, Tasgaon (part) and Miraj (part) tahsils has deep black soils capable of yielding bumper Kharip crops. These soils which are highly retentive of moisture also grow rabbi, jowar, wheat, gram and cash crops like sugarcane, turmeric, chillies, grapes etc. This central portion is thus the rich agriculture tract of the district. 3) The rest Eastern part of the district comprising miraj (part), Tasgaon (part), Khanapur (part) and whole of Atpadi, Kavathe mahankal and Jath tahsils has a shallow poor grey soils. Bajra, cotton, jowar are the main crops of this zone.

The district broadly can be divided into three macroclimatic zones as under

   i.   Western part of Shirala tahsil.

   ii. East Shirala, Walwa, Miraj (West), Tasgaon (West) and Khanapur (South-West).

   iii. Tahsil Khanapur, Atpadi, Kavathemahankal, Jath, Miraj (East) and Tasgaon (East).

The climate gets hotter and drier towards the East and humidity goes on increasing towards the West. The maximum temperature ranges between 31.1° C in July to 41.5°C in April. Similarly, the minimum temperature ranges from 10.3°C in December to 21.5°C from April to June. The percentage of humidity at 3.30 hours varies from 54 percent in March to 37 percent in August. Similarly, percentage of humidity at 17.30 hours varies from 30 percent in April to 69 percent in July. The rainfall and temperature have pronounced effects on climate.

Solapur district (Fig. 11) is situated on the South-East fringe of Maharashtra state and lies between 17° 10' and 18° 32' North latitude and 74° 42' and 75° 15' East longitude. Solapur district is surrounded by Ahmednagar and Osmanabad district in the North, Osmanabad district and Andra Pradesh in the East, Sangli district and the Karnataka state to the South and Satara and Pune districts towards the West. There is no important hill system in the district. Only in the North of Barshi tahsil several spurs of Balghat range pass South for a few miles. Of these, the chief is the Barshi ghat, about fourteen miles East of Barshi tahsil. The low table land and small separate hills in Kermala and Madha tahsils act as the watershed between Bhima river and Sina river.

The chief rivers of Solapur district includes Bhima with its right bank feeders Nira and Man left bank feeders the Sina and Bhogawati. The Bhima rises from the Sahyadries at Bhimashankar in Khed tashil of Pune district. The geographical foundation of soil revailing in Solapur district is mainly of Deccan trap of volcanic origin. The solun is underlain by partially decomposed basaltic rock, locally known as "MURUM" which overlies percent material. On account of more or less complete absence of leaching, the soils are base saturated, the exchangeable, calcium being the predominant claimant. The lime reserve is fairly high (3.5 to 10 p.c.). The soils exhibit varying degrees of erosion and truncated profile is a common occurrence.

The soils in the district can be classified into four main categories on the basis of depth and structure namely -

a) Very shallow soils with depth below 7.5 cm.

b) Shallow soils between 7.5 to 22.5 cm.

c) Medium deep soils between 22.5 to 90 cm.

d) Deep soils with depth more than 90 cm.

It is broadly estimated that out of the total cultivated area very shallow soils occupy about 10 percent of the area, shallow soils 20 percent medium deep soils 45 percent area and deep soils 25 percent area. In Karmala tahsil half the soils is black and the remaining is red and light. The soils of Sangola and Mangalweda are mainly light brown or greyisn black and are shallow. Madha tahsil has shallow soil having varying depth and quality. The soil in Malsiras is shallow and not retentive of moisture. Except along with the banks of the rivers and nallas and the few valleys where the soils are deep, district has shallow soils with low water holding capacity. Crops in this area, therefore, suffer the most during the drought conditions.

Climatically the entire district falls in the rain shadow area. The monsoon period in Solapur district cover the period from mid-June to end of September. There are two peaks in the rainfall pattern of the district. The first in June-July and the second in September with a through in between. The rainfall through out the district is scanty and annual average is about 580 mms. The meager rainfall is received from South West as well as North East monsoon. The paucity of total amount of rainfall and large variations both in extent and the distribution in different years makes the agriculture almost a gamble on the rains. There are variations in the total rainfall, but also the distribution of rainfall was unevenly spread over the monsoon seasons. The number of rainy days are varied from year to year.

Agro-climatically, the entire district except Akkalkot tahsil falls in the rainfall shadow zone. The total area under forest which is scattered i.e. 403.23 thorny buses. The forest area is much scattered. It may be roughly divided into two tracts, hills between Barshi and Osmanabad on the extreme North and East hills to the South of Malsairas and Sangola in the extreme South West. Solapur district comprises of an area of 15021 sq.km. which is 4.88 percent of the total area of the state. Of this, urban areas account for 414 sq.km and rural area for 14,607 sq.km. In terms of area Barshi is the largest tahsil with an area of 1,626 sq.km. and the smallest tahsil is North Solapur with an area of 736 sq.km.

In the present chapter three district of Southern Maharashtra namely, Kolhapur, Sangli and Solapur have been selected. These districts have been selected on the basis of geographical and climatical parameters. Secondly, these districts have great importance in sericulture business because, they adjoins the sericulturally developed states like Karnataka and Andhra Pradesh. In Kolhapur district, total area under mulberry cultivation is 299 acres with involvement of 10 tahsils, 130 villages and 341 farmers. In Sangli district sericulture is practised in 8 tahsils, including 80 villages and 174 farmers and area under mulberry cultivation is about 292.20 acre. While, in Solapur district mulberry is cultivated in 344 acres involving 7 tahsils, 63 villages and 312 farmers and produced 33 tons of raw silk. In the present study observations were made on rearing performance of silkworms (*B. mori* L. Pm x NB_4D_2) and cocoon production with respect to biotic factors such as diseases (Pebrine, Grassere (Fig. 61), Flacherie (Fig. 60) and Muscardine (Fig. 62) and pests uzifly (Fig. 65), other insects and vertebrate pests). As regards to abiopercent tic factors, climatic conditions of the districts have been considered which includes rainfall, temperature, humidity, light and quality of soil. For the experimental work 10 farmers have been selected for irrigated crops and ten for rainfed crops in each districts for rearing purpose. Observations were restricted on 100 dfls of each farmer for each crop through out the years, 2000 to 2002. The rearing performance was assessed with respect to number of cocoons produced, quality of cocoon, per kg weight of cocoons single cocoon weight, shell weight, harvesting duration and diseases and pests of silk worms. The observations on the silk worm rearing performance by the farmers from 3 districts have been studied. The larval duration and rendita of crops also have been assessed in three districts of Southern Maharashtra (Tables 5-10).

Table 5 : Average larval duration of silkworms in Kolhapur district in different seasons

Season	Month	Year			Average
		2000	2001	2002	
Winter	October	26.50	26.75	26.25	26.50
	November	27.25	27.50	27.25	27.25
	December	28.00	28.50	28.25	28.25
	January	28.75	28.50	28.25	28.50
Summer	February	24.75	24.25	24.50	24.50
	March	23.25	23.50	23.75	23.50
	April	22.50	22.75	22.25	22.50
	May	24.00	24.50	24.25	24.25
Rainy	June	22.50	22.75	22.25	22.50
	July	23.50	23.75	23.25	23.50
	August	24.50	24.75	24.25	24.50
	September	26.00	26.75	26.25	26.33

Table 6 : Average larval duration of silkworms in Sangli district in different seasons

Season	Month	Year			Average
		2000	2001	2002	
Winter	October	25.50	25.75	25.25	25.50
	November	26.25	26.50	26.75	26.50
	December	27.50	27.75	27.25	27.50
	January	27.75	27.50	27.25	27.50
Summer	February	23.75	23.50	23.25	23.50
	March	22.25	22.75	22.50	22.50
	April	21.50	21.25	21.75	23.25
	May	23.00	23.50	23.75	23.25
Rainy	June	21.50	22.75	22.50	22.50
	July	22.25	22.75	22.50	22.50
	August	23.50	23.75	23.25	23.50
	September	24.75	24.25	24.50	24.50

Table 7 : Average larval duration of silkworms in Solapur district in different seasons

Season	Month	Year			Average
		2000	2001	2002	
Winter	October	25.00	25.75	25.50	25.50
	November	26.00	26.50	26.25	26.25
	December	27.00	27.25	27.50	27.25
	January	27.00	27.50	27.25	27.25
Summer	February	23.00	23.25	23.50	23.25
	March	22.00	22.50	22.25	22.25
	April	21.00	21.25	21.50	21.25
	May	22.50	22.75	22.25	22.50
Rainy	June	21.00	21.25	21.50	21.25
	July	22.00	22.25	22.75	22.33
	August	23.00	23.50	23.75	23.50
	September	24.00	24.50	24.25	24.25

It has been observed that the number of cocoons produced per 100 dfls was highest in Solapur district, moderate in Sangli district and lowest in Kolhapur district. The same sequence was noticed with per kg cocoon weight and cocoon grades (Tables 8-10).

Table 8 : Cocoon characterization in Solapur district (Years 2000-2002)

	Cocoon wt.	Shell wt.	Rendita
Winter	1.15	0.160	9.32
Summer	0.96	0.120	8.98
Rainy	1.00	0.140	9.15
Ave	1.09	0.140	9.05

Table 9 : Cocoon characterization in Sangli district (Years 2000-2002)

	Cocoon wt.	Shell wt.	Rendita
Winter	1.20	0.162	9.10
Summer	0.96	0.130	8.98
Rainy	1.02	0.136	9.06
Ave	1.06	0.142	9.04

Table 10 : Cocoon characterization in Kolhapur district (Years 2000-2002)

	Cocoon wt.	Shell wt.	Rendita
Winter	1.3	0.162	9.20
Summer	0.94	0.115	9.50
Rainy	0.96	0.136	9.93
Ave	1.06	0.137	9.87

During the cource of study (years 2000 to 2002) it has been noticed that the incidence of Grasserie, Flacherie, and Muscardine diseases was very commen in all 3 districts of Southern Maharashtra. However, in Solapur districts incidence of diseases was very low, it was moderate in Sangli and highest in Kolhapur district.

In general Grasserie incidence was noticed from March and peaked in the month of July in all the districts selected for the present study. The incidence of Flacherie was also started from March and peaked in July and then declined as like Grasserie. Muscardine incidence was noticed from November and peaked in February and then declined. The results indicate that the incidence of Grassarie was highest in Solapur district, it was moderate in Sangli and lowest in Kolhapur district. The incidence of Flacherie was also highest in Solapur district and moderate in Sangli and lowest in Kolhapur. The incidence of Muscardine was

Table 11 : Pests of mulberry silkworm *B. mori* in Kolhapur district

Sr. No.	Common name	Generic name	Family	Order	Class	Occurrence
A)	PREDATORS					
1.	Dermestid beetles	*Dermestis cadverinus*	Demestidae	Coleoptera	Insecta	Sept. to Dec.
2.	Praying mantid	*Hierodula bipapilla*	Mantidae	Dictyoptera	Insecta	July to March
3.	Earwings		Forficulidae	Dermaptera	Insecta	June to Nov.
4.	Wasps	*Polistes hebraeus*	Vespidae	Hymenoptera	Insecta	June to Nov.
5.	Ants	*Oecophylla smaragdina*	Formicidae	Hymenoptera	Insecta	June to Nov.
6.	Sting bug	*Canthecona furcellata*	Pentatomidae	Hemiptera	Insecta	June to Nov.
7.	Ruduviid bug	*Sycanus collaris*	Reduviidae	Hemiptera	Insecta	June to Nov.
B)	PARASITOIDS					
8.	Ichneumonid	*Xanthopimpla pedator*	Ichneumonidae	Hymenoptera	Insecta	Sept. to Feb.
9.	Braconid fly	*Apanteles belippae*	Braconidae	Hymenoptera	Insecta	Sept. to Feb.
10.	Braconid fly	*A. stantoni*	Braconidae	Hymenoptera	Insecta	Sept. to Feb.
11.	Uzifly	*Exorista bombycis*	Tachinidae	Diptera	Insecta	Thr. out year
C)	VERTEBRATES					
12.	Cobra snake	*Naja naja*	Elapidae	Squamata	Reptilia	Nov. to June
13.	Rat snake	*Ptyas mucosus*	Elapidae	Squamata	Reptilia	Nov. to June
14.	Wall lizard	*Hemidactylus flaviviridis*	Gekkonidae	Squamata	Reptilia	Thr. out year

Contd...

Table 11 – Contd...

Sr. No.	Common name	Generic name	Family	Order	Class	Occurrence
15.	Garden lizard	*Calotes versicolor*	Agamidae	Squamata	Reptilia	Thr. out year
A)	AVES					
16.	Owl	*Bubo nipalensis*	Strigidae	Strigiformes	Aves	Thr. out year
17.	House sparrow	*Passer domesticus*	Plocediae	Passeriformes	Aves	Thr. out year
18.	Jungle crow	*Corvus splendens*	Corvidae	Passeriformes	Aves	Thr. out year
19.	Bulbul	*Pycnonotus jocosus*	Pycnonotidae	Passeriformes	Aves	Thr. out year
20.	Indian Mynah	*Acridotheres tristis*	Sturnidae	Passeriformes	Aves	Thr. out year
21.	Wagtail	*Motacilla alba*	Motacilidae	Passeriformes	Aves	Thr. out year
B)	MAMMALIA					
22.	Jackal	*Canis aureus*	Canidae	Carnivora	Mammalia	Thr. out year
23.	Fox	*Pteropus giguanteus*	Canidae	Carnivora	Mammalia	Thr. out year
24.	Monkey	*Macoca mulatta*	Ceropitheadae	Primate	Mammalia	Thr. out year
25.	Mouse	*Mus musculus*	Muridae	Rodentia	Mammalia	Thr. out year
26.	Rat	*Rattus rattus*	Muridae	Rodentia	Mammalia	Thr. out year
27.	Squirrel	*Funambulus palmarum*	Sciuridae	Rodentia	Mammalia	Thr. out year

Table 12 : Pests of mulberry silkworm *B. mori* in Sangli district

Sr. No.	Common name	Generic name	Family	Order	Class	Occurrence
A)	PREDATORS					
1.	Dermestid beetles	*Dermestis cadverinus*	Demestidae	Coleoptera	Insecta	Sept. to Dec.
2.	Praying mantid	*Hierodula bipapilla*	Mantidae	Dictyoptera	Insecta	July to March
3.	Earwings		Forficulidae	Dermaptera	Insecta	June to Nov.
4.	Wasps	*Polistes hebraeus*	Vespidae	Hymenoptera	Insecta	June to Nov.
5.	Ants	*Oecophylla smaragdina*	Formicidae	Hymenoptera	Insecta	June to Nov.
6.	Sting bug	*Canthecona furcellata*	Pentatomidae	Hemiptera	Insecta	June to Nov.
7.	Ruduviid bug	*Sycanus collaris*	Reduviidae	Hemiptera	Insecta	June to Nov.
B)	PARASITOIDS					
8.	Ichneumonid	*Xanthopimpla pedator*	Ichneumonidae	Hymenoptera	Insecta	Sept. to Feb.
9.	Braconid fly	*Apanteles belippae*	Braconidae	Hymenoptera	Insecta	Sept. to Feb.
10.	Braconid fly	*A. stantoni*	Braconidae	Hymenoptera	Insecta	Sept. to Feb.
11.	Uzifly	*Exorista bombycis*	Tachinidae	Diptera	Insecta	Thr. out year
C)	VERTEBRATES					
12.	Cobra snake	*Naja naja*	Elapidae	Squamata	Reptilia	Nov. to June
13.	Rat snake	*Ptyas mucosus*	Elapidae	Squamata	Reptilia	Nov. to June
14.	Wall lizard	*Hemidactylus flaviviridis*	Gekkonidae	Squamata	Reptilia	Thr. out year
15.	Garden lizard	*Calotes versicolor*	Agamidae	Squamata	Reptilia	Thr. out year

Contd...

Table 12 – Contd...

Sr. No.	Common name	Generic name	Family	Order	Class	Occurrence
A)	AVES					
16.	Owl	*Bubo nipalensis*	Strigidae	Strigiformes	Aves	Thr. out year
17.	House sparrow	*Passer domesticus*	Plocediae	Passeriformes	Aves	Thr. out year
18.	Jungle crow	*Corvus splendens*	Corvidae	Passeriformes	Aves	Thr. out year
19.	Bulbul	*Pycnonotus jocosus*	Pycnonotidae	Passeriformes	Aves	Thr. out year
20.	Indian Mynah	*Acridotheres tristis*	Sturnidae	Passeriformes	Aves	Thr. out year
B)	MAMMALIA					
21.	Jackal	*Canis aureus*	Canidae	Carnivora	Mammalia	Thr. out year
22.	Fox	*Pteropus giguanteus*	Canidae	Carnivora	Mammalia	Thr. out year
23.	Monkey	*Macoca mulatta*	Ceropitheadae	Primate	Mammalia	Thr. out year
24.	Mouse	*Mus musculus*	Muridae	Rodentia	Mammalia	Thr. out year
25.	Rat	*Rattus rattus*	Muridae	Rodentia	Mammalia	Thr. out year
26.	Squirrel	*Funambulus palmarum*	Sciuridae	Rodentia	Mammalia	Thr. out year

Table 13 : Pests of mulberry silkworm *B. mori* in Solapur district

Sr. No.	Common name	Generic name	Family	Order	Class	Occurrence
A)	PREDATORS					
1.	Dermestid beetles	*Dermestis cadverinus*	Demestidae	Coleoptera	Insecta	Sept. to Dec.
2.	Praying mantid	*Hierodula bipapilla*	Mantidae	Dictyoptera	Insecta	July to March
3.	Earwings		Forficulidae	Dermaptera	Insecta	June to Nov.
4.	Wasps	*Polistes hebraeus*	Vespidae	Hymenoptera	Insecta	June to Nov.
5.	Ants	*Oecophylla smaragdina*	Formicidae	Hymenoptera	Insecta	June to Nov.
6.	Sting bug	*Canthecona furcellata*	Pentatomidae	Hemiptera	Insecta	June to Nov.
B)	PARASITOIDS					
7.	Ichneumonid fly	*Xanthopimpla pedator*	Ichneumonidae	Hymenoptera	Insecta	Sept. to Feb.
8.	Braconid fly	*Apanteles belippae*	Braconidae	Hymenoptera	Insecta	Sept. to Feb.
9.	Braconid fly	*A. stantoni*	Braconidae	Hymenoptera	Insecta	Sept. to Feb.
10.	Uzifly	*Exorista bombycis*	Tachinidae	Diptera	Insecta	Thr. out year
C)	VERTEBRATES					
11.	Cobra snake	*Naja naja*	Elapidae	Squamata	Reptilia	Nov. to June
12.	Rat snake	*Ptyas mucosus*	Elapidae	Squamata	Reptilia	Nov. to June
13.	Wall lizard	*Hemidactylus flaviviridis*	Gekkonidae	Squamata	Reptilia	Thr. out year
14.	Garden lizard	*Calotes versicolor*	Agamidae	Squamata	Reptilia	Thr. out year

Contd...

Table 13 – Contd...

Sr. No.	Common name	Generic name	Family	Order	Class	Occurrence
A)	AVES					
15.	Owl	*Bubo nipalensis*	Strigidae	Strigiformes	Aves	Thr. out year
16.	House sparrow	*Passer domesticus*	Plocediae	Passeriformes	Aves	Thr. out year
17.	Jungle crow	*Corvus splendens*	Corvidae	Passeriformes	Aves	Thr. out year
18.	Bulbul	*Pycnonotus jocosus*	Pycnonotidae	Passeriformes	Aves	Thr. out year
19.	Indian Mynah	*Acridotheres tristis*	Sturnidae	Passeriformes	Aves	Thr. out year
20.	Wagtail	*Motacilla alba*	Motacillidae	Passeriformes	Aves	Thr. out year
B)	MAMMALIA					
21.	Jackal	*Canis aureus*	Canidae	Carnivora	Mammalia	Thr. out year
22.	Fox	*Pteropus giguanteus*	Canidae	Carnivora	Mammalia	Thr. out year
23.	Mouse	*Mus musculus*	Muridae	Rodentia	Mammalia	Thr. out year
24.	Rat	*Rattus rattus*	Muridae	Rodentia	Mammalia	Thr. out year
25.	Squirrel	*Funambulus palmarum*	Sciuridae	Rodentia	Mammalia	Thr. out year

highest in Kolhapur district, moderate in Sangli district and lowest in Solapur district.

Uzifly *Exorisita bombycis* (Louis) (Diptera) was the major pest in all three districts studied. Uzifly incidence was noticed through out the year at different rearing centres of three districts. However, its population peaked in February and June during the year. Incidence of uzifly was highest in Kolhapur district, moderate in Sangli and lowest in Solapur district. It has been observed that uzifly incidence was not found on rainfed crops of Solapur district but, it was noticed on the irrigated crops of sericulture. In Sangli and Kolhapur districts uzifly was well established. In fact in Kolhapur district, it caused severe losses to crops (62%). Uzi infected larvae are shown in (Fig. 63), pupae and uzifly trap are also shown in (Figs. 64 and 67) respectively.

Other insect and vertebrate pests associated with mulberry silkworm (*B. mori*) are listed in (Tables 11-13). The prominent pests observed in all three districts were ants (Fig. 66), wall-lizzards, snakes, frog, rat, wasps etc. From the pest kedar only uzifly was dangerous and dominant over all pests species.

The data on temperature, humidity, light and rainfall of three districts is represented in Figures 68 to 70.

In case of rainfed rearing performance of silkworms, cocoon quality was found inferior to irrigated crop by shell weight, single cocoon weight, larval duration, rendita and cocoon size and shape. However, the pattern of incidence of diseases and pests was same.

In addition to the selected farmers (ten in each centre) about 350 farmers from Solapur, 235 farmers from Sangli and 300 farmers from Kolhapur district have been consulted through questionnaire. It was found that in the rearing farms of these farmers, the same trend of incidence of diseases and pests was noticed as in selected farmers.

During the course of study it was observed that some farmers harvested only two to five crops in a year. Minimum number of harvestation of crops was observed in Solapur district, it was moderate in Sangli and low in Kolhapur district. The main reasons of taking less number of crops were insufficient water source and climatic conditions such as high temperature, low rainfall and fluctuating humidity, etc. During the course of study the selected farmers used N:P:K, 300:148:148 kg/ha/year in 5 split doses and 30 mt farm yard manure per/ha/year in two split doses.

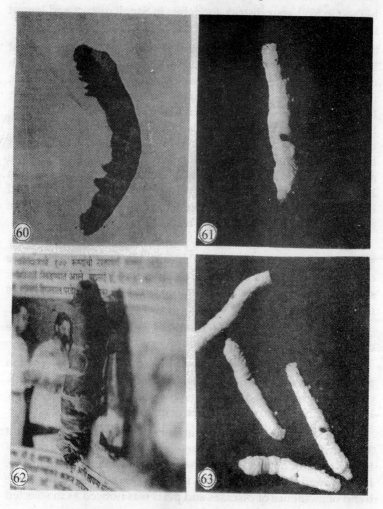

PLATE 15

Fig. 60 : Infected larva with flacherie; Fig. 61 : Infected larva with
Grassarie; Fig. 62 : Infected larva with Muscardine;
Fig. 63 : Infected larvae with uzi-fly

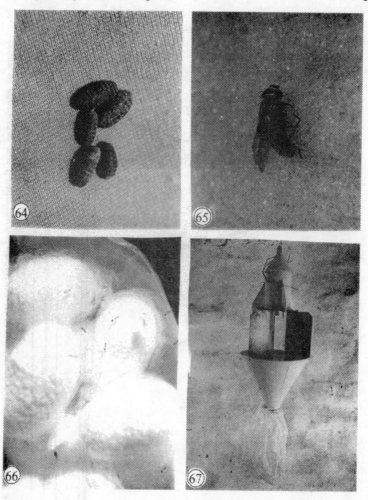

PLATE 16

Fig. 64 : Uzi-fly cocoons; Fig. 65 : Adult Uzi-fly;
Fig. 66 : Cocoons with Ants (natural enemies); Fig. 67 : Uzi-fly trap

Shoot Feeding and Sericultural Trends

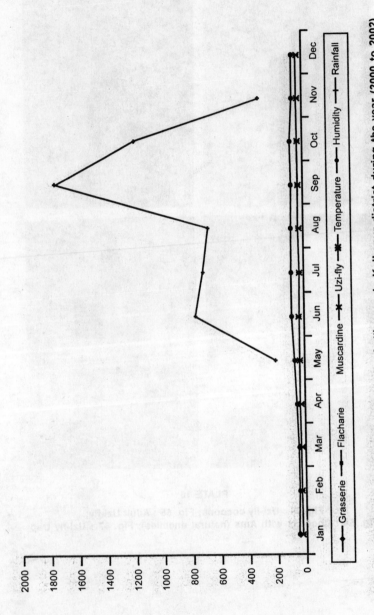

Fig. 68 : Incidence of diseases and pests of silkworm in Kolhapur district during the year (2000 to 2002)

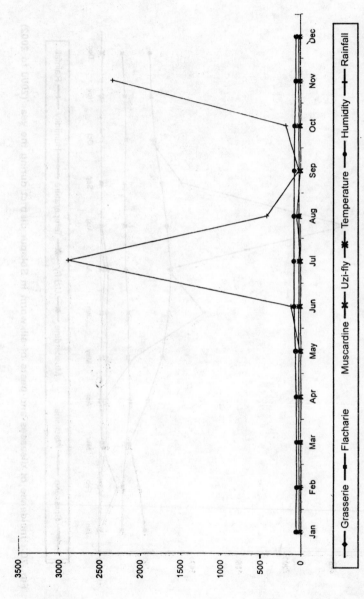

Fig. 69 : Incidence of diseases and pests of silkworm in Sangli district during the year (2000 to 2002)

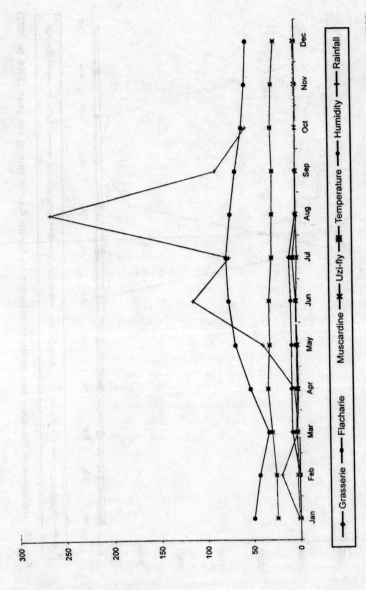

Fig. 70 : Incidence of diseases and pests of silkworm in Solapur district during the year (2000 to 2002)

5

REARING TRENDS IN SILKWORM

Narayanan and Chawla (1965) have reported the effect of frequency of feeding on the growth and development in two races of silkworm; local Mysore and Shungetsu hosh. Their statistical analysis indicated that there is no significant difference between the number and method of feeding and single cocoon weight, single shell weight, floss percentage, filament length and denier.

Tayade (1981) studied the rearing performance of silk worms, B. mori with respect to mulberry varieties and cocoon quality. He reported that the larval duration was not affected in Marathwada region even when the larvae were fed with different qualities of leaf. The single cocoon weight was observed to be higher in the larvae fed with tender leaves of 5.54 followed by mixed and tender leaves LM-2. In the present study M-5 variety of mulberry have been consider in all three districts viz. Kolhapur, Sangli and Solapur for the assessment of rearing performance of silkworms (B. mori). It was observed that cocoon quality was better in Solapur district than that of the Sangli and Kolhapur districts.

Krishnaswamy et al. (1971) studied the mulberry leaf quality and silk production by providing additional three proteins, (casein, egg substance and milk powder), one amino acid (glycine), two vitamins, (ascorbic acid and folic acid) and two sugars (glucose and molasses). Their results indicated good effect of feeding atleast with six of them resulting in better growth of silkworm and higher silk production. Out of the four seasons they tried, three seasons showed almost similar results. However, no such clear effect was observed during the adverse season. In the present study no additional component have been utilized to mulberry leaves for the assessment of rearing performance of silkworms in Southern Maharashtra (three districts only).

Sengupta *et al.* (1974) studied the effect of spacing of silkworm larvae and cocoon characterization of some multivoltine breeds of silkworm *B. mori.* They reported that in trays of 2.5' x 2' the characters progressively improved when the number of larvae were brought down from 400 to 100; in general, the groups 100-200 behaved much better. This trend in many cases existed up to 300 worms per tray. On this basis the requirement of space per 100 dfls reared (30,000 larvae after 4th moult) came to about 500 sq. ft.. This was based on cellular rearing, a spacing of two-thirds of it or 300-350 sq. ft. per 100 dfls have been recommended for bulk commercial rearing. In the present study standard spacing of silkworm larvae have been maintained and the multivoltine race Pm X NB$_4$D$_2$ was adopted for rearing performance.

Tayade (1978) studied the economic characters of cocoon with respect to mulberry variety as a quality difference of leaves. He observed that leaves of S-54 variety were superior in improving the cocoon weight and cocoon yield. He also studied the possibilities of rearing mulberry silkworms under Marathwada conditions and worked out the profitability ratio for input/output as 1:2.54. Very first time such a large scale commercial rearing was conducted by the Marathwada Agricultural University, Parbhani during Jan./Feb. 1979; 400 dfls were reared and 117 kgs cocoons were produced. The mass rearing was started from September, 1977 onwards providing chopped mulberry leaves in the early stage and entire leaves during the later stages, in sufficient quantity at the rate of four feedings/day. During 1978-79 about 150 farmers were involved in cultivation of mulberry in an area of 180 acres in Marathwada (Tayade, 1978). The sericulture in Western Maharashtra in Solapur district have been started in 1982 and the district is now leading in Southern Maharashtra.

Tayade (1983) studied the feasibility of rearing of multivotline and bivoltine races and their hybrids in Marathwada and reported that the summer rearing was not economical due to high temperature (average 39°C) prevailing in the Marathwada region. Further, he indicated that 25 farmers during 1978-79 had taken up mulberry plantation for the first time in about 105 acres and most of them paid due attention and produced satisfactory cocoon yield. Sericulture enterprise was in a critical stage due to lack of proper organization, poor follow-up action, want of technical guidance, irregular supply of laying, lower price of the cocoons and scattered mulberry plantation affected the expansion of sericulture industry in Marathwada.

Tayade (1983) studied different multivoltine, bivoltine races and their hybrids which revealed the possibilities of rearing mulberry silkworm successfully from July to March except summer conditions when temperature goes upto 39°C. The overall results indicated that the bivoltine and their hybrids were superior in yield and quality and the rearing results were better during monsoon and winter seasons. Tayade (1983) also discussed on three years economics of mulberry silkworm under partial irrigated conditions for one ha. of mulberry garden, which required 3000 dfls in 4 batches. The production was 1,125 kgs cocoons in a year. The gross income from 1 ha. mulberry garden was Rs. 22,500/- (Rs. 20/kg. cocoon) while the average cost of cultivation and silkworm rearing was Rs. 9,320.58 with the net profit of Rs. 13,979.42 and the ratio of input:output was 1:2.41. Tayade and Jawale (1984) also studied the comparative merits of 4 varieties of mulberry viz., K2, S-34, Kosen and LM2 and their effect on the cocoon qualities of bivoltine race i.e. NB7, NB18 and hybrid race (Pm X NB 18). Their results indicated that the S-54 mulberry variety showed higher values in characters like larval duration, larval weight, single cocoon weight and cocoon yield. The hybrid Pm x NB 18 was superior in cocoon yield. In the present study, particularly in Solapur district 6 to 12 crops have been harvested in irrigated system and on rainfed condition only 2 to 4 crops were possible.

Behura and Panda (1984) studied the rearing performance of five multivoltine races of the mulberry silkworm B. mori, in Orissa and gave an account of the comparative rearing performance of the multivoltine races L2+3(O), Yellow, Oval (S), M3 and HM of B. mori, a species that was not reared usually for silk production in the state. Their results indicated that the larval growth was slow and mortality high in all the five races. According to them this was possibly because of the low protein content of the mulberry leaves on which they were fed, and also because of extreme fluctuations of temperature and humidity and diseases. In the present study in Solapur district larval development was faster than other two districts. This may be probably due to the favourable temperature, humidity and less attack of diseases, specially muscardine and flacherie except summer seasons.

Teli *et al.* (1984) observed that bivoltine hybrids (NB7 X NB18) were more efficient than Wai strains (Wai-1 and Wai-4) in silk production. But, larvae of the hybrids were more susceptible to diseases than those of the Wai strains.

Sathe *et al.* (1998) studied life table statistics and intrinsic rate of increase in Wai-4 *B. mori.* They reported that under laboratory conditions (25±2C, 80% R.H. 16 hrs photoperiod), the longevity of ovipositing females averaged 6.5 days (range, 5 to 8 days), the progeny production averaged 134.8 (range 61-300) adults with average sex ratio (male: female) 1 :0922 (range 1:0.76 to 1: 1.375), and the average length of immature stages was 43 days. The maximum mean progeny production per day (Mx) was 32.8 on 2nd day, the intrinsic rate of increase 'rm' per female per day was 0.097 and population multiplied 64.7 times, in mean generation time of 42.98 days. Present study was carried out in field conditions and rearing of silkworms *B. mori.* (Pm x NB_4D_2) have been assessed with respect to biotic and abiotic factors.

Karaivanov *et al.* (1985) studied the rearing performance of silkworms with respect to a biotic and aboitic factors. They reported that during the spring of the years 1982 and 1983 efforts have been made to remove the negative effects. The disturbed environmental factors and technological properties in silkworm hybrids affected rearing. They recommended strict maintenance during the first instars of higher temperature and humidity and during the last instars at lower temperature and humidity, with regular feeding and ventilation.

The field scale performance of hybrids in terms of cocoon yield/100 dfls through fortnightly observations was best during the first fortnight of December. The seasonal performance was best during the winter season with 32.398, 31.195 and 24.650 kg cocoons per 100 dfls for Pm x NB$_4$D$_2$, Pm x NB18 and Pm x C. *nichi*, respectively and the same was lowest during summer season with 18.666 and 8.590 kg cocoons per 100 dfls for Pm x NB$_4$D$_2$ and Pm x NB18, respectively. The *Pm* x *C. nichi* performed well during summer (16.407 kg) compared to its results during rainy season (15.383 kg) (Visweswara Gowda and Ravi, 1986).

Singh and Mavi (1986) studied the yield and quality of silk during spring and autumn in Punjab, India. There were 3 spring crops and 1 autumn crop. During the first spring crop, the maximum temperature was 25.8°C and the minimum 23.9°C and relative humidity was 90.9% as a favourable condition for the survival and development of larvae. During this period the quality of the mulberry leaves was at its maximum (48.29). The autumn crop was more favourable for the development of larvae than the 2nd and 3rd spring crops. The quantity and quality of silk was best in the post spring crop followed by the autumn crop and was lowest in the 2nd and 3rd spring crops. Singh and Mavi (1986) concluded that it was not economical to harvest the 2nd and 3rd spring crops.

Tayade (1987) studied the heterosis in silkworms by using both the mid parental and better parental values for reproductive, developmental and production (economic) trails of 12 hybrids and indicated that none of the cross showed significant, positive heterosis either over mid parent or better parent for percentage hatching. He further reported that the bivoltine hybrids NB$_7$ X NB$_4$D$_2$, NB$_{18}$ X NB$_3$D$_2$, and NB$_7$ X NB$_{18}$ and their reciprocals also performed better as far as number of eggs laid, hatching percentage, weight of silk gland, shell weight and filament length is concern. Among the parents, NB7 and NB18 were slightly higher in percent mean performance for all the characters. The multi parent HM was statistically inferior for all the characters studied over other parents and hybrids. Jawale and Tayade (1987) studied the effect of bed disinfectants viz. Bemoic acid, Kaolen, N.F., Paraformaldehyde, Turmeric powder, Lime and cleaned leaves with cotton on the growth with respect to disease control of silkworm B. mori. Their results indicate that disease control of silkworms showed useful effect on the silkworm growth, silk production and minimized disease incidence. The paraformaldehyde and cleaned leaves with cotton were found to be superior over other treatments. In present study paraformaldehyde and Vijetha were used as a disinfectants.

Sudhakaran and Nagaraj (1989) reported that the climatic and ecological conditions in hilly areas of Kerala were highly suitable for mulberry cultivation and silkworm rearing. They further reported that the development programmes of various service organizations and the response shown by the local farmers in mulberry cultivation led to the increase in cocoon production. The state government established reeling units and cocoon purchasing centres in all the district headquarters to support the increased cocoon production. Sericulture generated employment in the rural areas. Continuous support of CSRTI and the programme by the state government, made sericulture in Kerala, vibrant and confident.

Nahar *et al.* (1989) investigated the performance of some hybrids of mulberry silkworm, *B. mori* in Konkan. Their results indicated that the number of eggs per laying was maximum in CCI X NB18 (678) followed by that in (A2 X NB18 (672)). The maximum larval developmental period was 35.3 days for the race NB7 X NB18 while, it was minimum for 30.3 days NB_4D_2 X PCN. They concluded that the race NB7 X NB18 was the best over all with respect to survival percentage (94.2), weight of 10 green cocoons (11.83g), weight of 10 dry cocoons (6.18g) and weight of 10 silk shells (2.14g). The number of cocoons/kg was also minimum in NB7 X NB18 and yield of cocoon/100 dfls was higher in NB7 X NB18 (45.48kg) followed by CCI X NB18, NB_4D_2 X PCN, CA2 X NB18 and MYS X NB18. Finally, they concluded that NB7 X NB18 and CA2 X NB18 were found superior to the rest of the hybrids.

Thiagarajan *et al.* (1992) described the field performance of two commercial hybrids (Pm x NB18; Pm x NB_4D_2) of silkworm in Vidarbha region of Maharashtra state. Thiagarajan *et al.* (1994) have studied, the rearing of silkworm strains with most suited seasons in the year. Their results indicated that the following strains were found to be most suitable for rearing during particular seasons, viz. European 14M (spring) JC2p (Summer), M2 (autumn).

Gangwar *et al.* (1993) reported that ingestion, leaf withering rate and environmental factors (temp. & relative humidity) of silkworm rearing houses, when compared control revealed that higher temperature and lower humidity prevailing during hot hours of the day accelerated leaf withering (leaf moisture loss) leading to lower rate of ingestion by silkworm during hot periods of the day. The view opened new vistas of revising the quantum of leaf to be fed during each feed depending upon the room temperature and relative humidity of the rearing house.

Balavenkatasubbaiah *et al.* (1994) studied the efficacy of bleaching powder as a disinfectant against the patogens of silkworm *B. mori*. They reported that bleaching powder in 4.25% were found to be more effective than 2% formalin against *Nuclear Polyhedrosis virus, Beauveria bassiana, Nosema bombycis* and *Bacillus thuringiensis.*

Light is the major environmental factor that influences the physiological activities including the hatching in the silkworm, *B. mori* (Sivarami Reddy, 1993). Prolonged oviposition (up to 16h) and improper incubation may result in irregular hatching which can be overcome by keeping the eggs in darkness called 'black boxing', at eye-spot or blue egg stage (Datta, 1992) and later exposing them to light for uniform hatching. However, reports are available on the technique resulted in prolonged hatching (up to 48h) under farmers conditions for which, they attempted to prolong the black-boxing to the extent of 24h for synchronized hatching. However, scientific information is not available regarding the race specific post pavement duration of egg release from black-box and its effect on the hatching patterns and the rearing performance.

Meenal *et al.* (1994) studied the role of light during incubation of silkworm eggs and its effect on rearing performance and diapause. They reported that for uniform and perfect hatching eggs should be incubated under 12018 light regime. Light condition during incubation does not have any significant effect on rearing. The eggs incubated under short day conditions produced adult females which laid non-hibernating eggs in the next generation. It is advisable to provide minimum 12h light/day during incubation to minimize the occurrence of non-hibernating eggs.

Muniraju *et al.* (2001) studied effect of delayed brushing of black-boxed eggs on hatching and rearing performance in silkworm, *B. mori*. Their results indicated that silkworm eggs were black-boxed at pin-head or at blue-egg stage (8th or 9th day of oviposition) to get uniform and maximum hatching in a short duration on the expected day of hatching (10th day). Rearers have attempted to postpone the release of eggs from black-box to avoid irregular hatching. Delayed release from black-box and exposure to light was carried out to understand its impact on hatching patterns and rearing performance of the silkworm, *B. mori*. Results indicated that exposure of black-boxed eggs to light could be postponed up to 24h from the expected time of hatching to get maximum hatching without any adverse effect on the rearing performance. Rhythmic patterns in hatching of *B. mori* eggs influenced by photoperiods have been reported from both temperate and tropical countries (Takami, 1969; Sivarami Reddy *et al.*, 1998). Ananthanarayana *et al.* (1978) recorded hatching pattern reaching its peak in Pure Mysore breed of *B. mori* being very close to down under alternate light dark (LD) cycles. These observations corroborated with those of Sivarami Reddy and Sasira Baba (1990) and Sivarami Reddy *et al.* (1984) who opined that hatching during early down might be due to relative cooler condition with higher humidity, which minimizes the risk of desiccation.

The egg hatching peaks were observed on the initiation of the down or on exposing to the light zone hatched after reaching the next allowed zone or gate (Skopik and Pittendrigh, 1967). Darkness (free running stage) followed by light stimulus during early hours of the day of hatching (interruption of DD) is in practice to get maximum hatching (Benchamin and Nagaraj, 1987). Such experiments on the hatching rhythm under dark have been carried out in many cases (Fugo *et al.*, 1984; Sivarami Reddy, 1993).

Kamble (1998) studied the effect of cold storage on hatchability of cross breed and acid treated bivoltine eggs of silkworm, *B. mori*. He reported that simple refrigeration was the only technique for preserving the multi x bivoltine hybrid eggs and acid treated bivoltine hybrids. To study the effect of refrigeration on hatching an experiment was conducted by using multix bi hybrid (MY1 X CCl) and acid treated bivoltine hybrid (CCl X NB_4D_2). Eggs of different age groups (24, 48 and 72h) were consigned at 5°C, 2.5°C for different duration of 20, 30, 40, 50 & 60 days. His results showed that early embryonic stages (24h) can tolerate longer duration of refrigeration for a maximum period of 40 days in case of MY1 X CCI, whereas 48 & 72h old eggs can tolerate refrigeration for 20 days at 5°C and for 30 days at 2.5°C. In case of acid treated bivoltine hybrids, 24h old eggs can be preserved for 30 days at 5°C while 48 & 72h old eggs can be preserved for 20 days only.

Jingade *et al.* (2000) studied the hatching pattern and embryonic growth of the pigmented eggs in the non-diapausing multivoltine race, pure Mysure, of the silkworm, *B. mori.* Their results indicated that the embryonic stages delayed embryonic growth which resulted in hatching spread over a period of seventeen days.

Jayaswal and Raut (2000) studied the influence of low temperature incubation on diapause incidence and quantitative traits in *B. mori* (Multivoltine breed G-race). Their results revealed that the percentage incidence of diapause layings during December-January, January-February and February-March was significantly higher in the treatment (11.74 to 38.30) exposed to the normal temperature incubation that noted (0.59-7.11%) in the treatment of the low temperature incubation. In addition, larval period (626.668h), larval weight (33.58-37.45g) and cocoon weight (1.35-1.50g) during the said three seasons and shell weight (0.199-0.218g) during two of the said three seasons were also found to be significantly higher in the case of the normal incubated batch than those of the low temperature incubated one. The results implied that larval period, larval weight, cocoon weight and shell weight had a positive relationship with the incidence of diapause layings oviposited by the resultant moths.

Katti *et al.* (2001) studied the seasonal variation in fecundity and hatching in some popular races of *B. mori.* Their results indicated that both fecundity and hatching vary with the race and season. Maximum fecundity of 611 was observed in NB18 closely followed by KA(593), NB7 (93.59), NB_4D_2 (93.41) and NB18 (92.58) although the difference was marginal. All races except KA showed maximum fecundity during rainy season followed by winter and lowest during summer. However, in KA the highest fecundity was recorded during winter with marginally less fecundity in rainy and lowest during summer season. For the trait hatching %, all the races exhibited more hatching during rainy followed by winter and least during summer seasons. The success of cocoon crop depends upon the quality of silkworm seed (Narsimhanna, 1988). Proper hatching and rich laying increase the yield at the first instance. During incubation the embryo develops within the egg until hatching. This is easily influenced by various environmental factors like temperature, humidity, day length, etc. besides silkworm race (Tanaka, 1961; Benchamin & Krishnaswamy, 1981; Subba Rao *et al.*, 1987).

In silkworm, it is well known that most of the economic characters are quantitative in nature, phenotypic expression of which is greatly influenced by environmental factors such as temperature, humidity, and nutrition. Several workers have reported that oviposition in silkworm is influenced by nutrition, atmosphere, mating and laying condition (Yakayama, 1963; Siddhu *et al.*, 1967). Fecundity is influenced by both exogenous and endogenous factors besides genetic set up. Studies on the seasonal impact on the fecundity and hatching have shown that these two traits are easily influenced by seasons. Both fecundity and hatching vary with the season and race. Benchamin *et al.* (1990) reported that fecundity was high in winter and low in summer. Tayade *et al.* (1987) have reported that hatching in pure race was higher than hybrid. They also reported that hatching was vary with mulberry variety and mating time.

The seasonal variation in manifestation of characters was purely because of the environmental influence which not only affected silkworm directly but also the quality of leaf and metabolic activities in the silkworm. One of the prerequisites of successful seed production is the maintenance of the parental races as per the norms fixed at various levels of multiplication (Krishnaswamy, 1986; Narasimhanna, 1988).

An investigation was carried out by Das *et al.* (1990) to assess the feeding quality of three improved varieties of mulberry (536, 841 and 854) over Kanva-2 by silkworm feeding trails in different seasons. In general, the three improved varieties were found to be superior over Kanva-2 as assessed by the rearing performance. However, the variety S-54 was found to be the best among all. The best rearing results were obtained during August to January while April to May yielded the least values with regards to all economic characters. The mean larval weight with the variety S-36 (V4) was found to be significantly increased over Kanva-2 (VI) and S-54 (V2) while no such significant difference in the larval weight was recorded between S-36 and S-41. The highest to the lowest larval weight was obtained in the following order of farmers : V4 > V3 > V2 > V1.

As regards the ERR by number and by weight, percentage of larval pupation and larval growth index values the best results were obtained with the variety S-54 (V2). The mean values of these economic characters with S-54 (V2) were significant over Kanva - 2 (VI), S-41 (V3) and S-36 (V4). However, the variety Kanva-2 (VI) also showed greater mean values over S-41 (V3) and S-36 (V4) regarding ERR by number and by weight and growth index values of ERR were in the following order of treatments V2> V1>V3>V4> while that of larval pupation was V2>V3>V1>V4. There was no effect of varieties on the larval duration as the mean values did not showed any significant difference between varieties. However, the larval duration varied significantly due to seasonal change. The mean values of single cocoon weight due to varieties did not showed much variation. However, S-41 (V3) and Kanva-2 (VI) gave significantly higher cocoon weight than S-54 (V2). The cocoon weight obtained due to the variety S-36 (V4) was also on par with Kanva-2 and S-41.

As regards to single shell weight and shell percentage, the varieties S-41 (V3) and S-36 (V4) gave highest shell weight and shell percentage respectively. The highest to the lowest shell percentage was obtained in the following order of treatments V4>V2>V3>V1.

The maximum and the minimum larval weight were observed during the months of August-September 1985 (T4) and April-May 1984 (T1), respectively, irrespective of different varieties. The interaction between varieties and seasons were highest with V4T4 combination and was significant over all combinations. Regarding ERR by number and by weight, percentage of pupation, larval growth index values, the maximum and the minimum mean values were obtained in the months of December 1985, January 1986 (T5) and April-May 1984 respectively. Seasonal change had a significant effect on the larval duration also as the maximum larval period was required during January-February 1986 (T6). The maximum and the minimum cocoon weight, shell weight and shell percentage were obtained during December 1985-January 1986 (T5) and April-May 1984 (T1), respectively irrespective of varietal feeding. In the present study cocoon weight and shell weight have been studied and the results indicated that single cocoon weight and shell weight were highest in winter and lowest in summer. These results are in agreement with the results of Radhakrishna *et al.* (2001). In the present study it has been also observed that single cocoon weight and shell weight was higher in Solapur than other districts studied.

The importance of quality of leaf on growth, development and health of silkworm has been greatly stressed by Yokayama (1963). Leaf moisture content was crucial factor in production of good cocoon and which in lesser quantity was responsible for poor growth of worms. Dietary moisture level was an important factor in plant-herbivore interaction has also been stressed by Reese and Beck (1978). Decrease in water content of food affected nitrogen utilization efficiency and led to poor growth of consumer insects (Scriber, 1978). S36 and S41 varieties of mulberry leaves showed higher values of leaf moisture content. This higher content of moisture in the leaves appears to be the conducive factor for better larval growth and higher shell weight. Narayanaprakash *et al.* (1985) also reported significant increase in the larval weight of silkworm with the increase in leaf moisture content.

Thiagarajan *et al.* (1991) reported that the silk quality was superior and the larval quality was inferior in spring, strong larval quality but weak cocoon and silk qualities resorted to in summer and autumn. Indian sericultural research institutions have developed silkworm races suited to the conditions prevailing in our country and cocoon with greater silk content by judiciously utilizing the different combinations in different seasons.

The concept and techniques of chawki silkworm rearing and principles of management of chawki rearing centres are well known to both sericologists and sericulturists (Benchamin, 1992). Chawki silkworm rearing has given special attention because of the following attributes

1. Young silkworms require the best care of food, environment and hygiene as compared to late age.

2. Young silkworms grow at much faster rate then late age and over all growth is interstadia dependent.

3. Healthy and robust young silkworms are strong enough to resist diseases and cope the adverse rearing conditions later.

4. It is easy, economic and efficient to organise young silkworm rearing activities collectively.

5. It relieves the sericulturists for a period of two week (one week of egg incubation and another week of chawki rearing) for other works.

6. The management of large scale farm becomes easy and more efficient with the linkage to chawki rearing centres.

Good chawki rearing is the first step towards successful silkworm crop. Scientific chawki rearing has been the main emphasis in the new technology of silkworm rearing, advocated in 1970s. Organization of chawki rearing centres formed the focus of all development schemes in sericulture, subsequently, covered under five year plans. World Bank assisted Karnataka Sericulture Project and National Sericulture Project. There are about 2000 chawki rearing centres in the country presently. Majority of them are functioning in Karnataka. It is proposed to strengthen this activity by establishing additional CRC units under NSP and 10th five year plane. Benchamin (1992) reported that chawki rearing is highly desirable that all the sericulturists should be given chawki worms instead of layings. The task of organizing more centres for this purpose, is quite challenging. It is inevitable therefore to share this responsibility with the private sectors. In Japan, CRC's covered more than 92% of the total young age rearing of the country and the entire activity was organized in the private sector. In India also young silkworm rearing can be organized into a commercial venture in the private sector. But this sector should be made more profitable in comparison with regular silkworm rearing.

The chawki rearing as a full time vocation is a less attractive venture. Mainly because of the low yield leaf suitable for chawki and the low selling price of chawki reared worms. Even to get the same income as that from regular rearing, the chawki selling price should be increased to rupees 800 per 100 layings. If it is raised to Rs. 90 per 100 layings of chawki reared worms, then the additional income of Rs. 5,900, may attract enough sericulturists to take up chawki rearing as a full time occupation (Benchamim, 1992). The price of chawki worms may also be linked to the average price of one kg of cocoon in the market.

Majority of the existing CRCs were run by the Government agencies (Benchamin, 1992). The chawki rearing charges ranged from more than Rs. 20 to Rs. 60 per 100 layings. Apart from causing great financial loss to the Government every year, the impact of such centres was also poor because of the poor management and low quality of worms raised in these centres. Following are the reasons for poor performance of CRCs in India. (1) Lack of well maintained chawki garden, (2) Ineffective disinfections, (3) Poor infrastructure, (4) Partial adoption of rearing techniques, (5) Inadequaie man power, (6) Poor technical know-how of workers, (7) Sporadic distribution of centres. The policy of establishing additional CRCs under Government sector, therefore needs a through review.

There are a number of Private CRCs functioning in Karnaiaka State. They do make a high margin of profit. A recent study clearly showed that many practices followed in private CRCs were highly profit oriented and at the cost of men, material and care required during chawki rearing. In Maharashtra chawki rearing centres are badly needed either from government or private agencies for development of sericultural activities. However, BAIF in Maharashtra is trying for providing chawki rearing facilities to the silkworm rearers.

Krishnaswami (1980) investigated improved method of rearing of young age silkworms. In addition, several workers (CSR & TI 1971, Chikkanna et al., 1993; Vineet Kumar et al., 1994) attempted chawki rearing in India. Chikkanna et al. (1993) reported that crops raised from chawki reared batches showed better performance in terms of higher cocoon yield/100 dfls in both bivoltine and cross breeds as compared to direct seed distribution. As regards to the monetary returns, the cocoons raised from chawki batches received higher price indicating better quality of cocoons. Season wise performance comparison of silkworm crops raised from chawki reared batches and directly distributed seeds indicate the benefit, both in terms of yield and returns, obtained through chawki rearing. During 1992-93, 40 CRCs were in operation under the technical guidance of Research Extension centres of CSR & TI, Mysore and 38,026 bivoltine and 5,62,108 cross breed chawki reared dfls were supplied to getting an average cocoon yield of 35.68 and 36.65 kg/100 dfls, respectively. In addition, 80,683 bivoltine and 3,91,390 cross breed dfls were also distributed directly to the farmers and an average yield of 28.83 and 29.54 kg/ 100 dfls, respectively was recorded. Above data clearly indicates that farmers still fulfil their demand through direct distribution. Here, it must be noted that this is a general trend, throughout, irrespective of areas where extension centres or private CRCs are operating. Why it is so? It is due to unawareness of sericulturists/ organizational failure/insufficient chawki management/higher service charges or this system itself is technically inappropriate? Is it not that because of this trend, sericulture industry is loosing in terms of raw silk production? The reasons for same need to be located and overcome. However, what is immediately needed is to popularize CRC programme through concerted efforts by extension personnel. Chikkanna *et al.* (1993) made few suggestions.

1. Sericulturists should be educated about CRC programmes using simple and attractive charts, slides, figures etc. highlighting advantages of the programmes such as, i) Higher cocoon yield; ii) Higher rate of returns; iii) Labour and time economy and iv) Timely and adequate benefits/ assured crop yield even in adverse conditions etc.

2. While conducting group discussion with the farmers, the data from figures presented or similar such results could be quoted, and also of figures obtained from programmes conducted locally, to convince and educate the farmers on the importance of the programme and need for its systematic functioning.

3. Correct and apt way of organizing and running of the chawki rearing programme should be explained to the villagers highlighting: i) Chawki rearing schedules, collection of indents, timely procurement of dfls ii) On earmarking suitable well ventilated house for chawki rearing and maintaining separate chawki garden properly iii) On organizing collective disinfection for every batch of crop also at chawki rearing centres. iv) Follow up of rearing at farmers place after distribution of Chawki reared dfls and educating them regularly on prophylactic and diseases control measures.

The silkworm, *B. mori* is a monophogous insect which feeds on mulberry leaves. Jelmoni (1943) has given a data on mulberry leaf yield obtained as a result of various kinds of agronomical practices. Among all, allowing mulberry plant to sprout at a height of 50 cm from the ground level resulted in highest production per hectare. Sato (1968) has shown the mulberry plants cut to a height of about 40 cm above the top of stump (Kabuage training) gave more leaf yield than the one which was cut at the base of shoots (Negari training). Later, Iwata (1978, 1981) have also proven that between, two pruning methods viz., cutting off plants to a height of 10 cm and 35 cm from the ground level, the latter gave better branching, better branch growth and also more leaf yield as compared to former. Biochemical analysis has revealed that there was a significant increase in soluble sugar and starch contents in the leaf of high stem pruning (35 cm above the ground level) as compared to basal pruning (Annonymous, 1987).

It is evident that the quality and quantity of mulberry leaf varied under two systems of pruning. Zubayri (1983) did not observed significant difference in rearing performance of silkworm hybrids on continuous feeding throughout larval life with mulberry leaf from basal pruned and high stem pruned (35 cm. above ground level) plants. However, nutritional requirements in young and late age silkworm rearing vary and carbohydrate of mulberry leaf is very important element for the healthy growth of silkworm, especially for the healthy growth of silkworm, especially for keeping healthy growth of infant larvae. Vinod Kumar and Benchamin (1990) studied the mulberry leaf quality under two systems of pruning for young and late age silkworm rearing. They reported that survival rate, cocoon yield and absolute silk content of bivoltine hybrid (NB18 X NB7) were significantly increased by 11.5, 17.0 and 18.07 respectively, in treatment batch [feeding of young age (I-III instars) and late age (IV-V instars) silkworm on high stem pruned (35 cm above ground level) and basal pruned plants respectively] as compared to control batch (continuous feeding on basal pruned plants throughout larval life).

Narasinha Murthy and Subramanyam (1988) studied the effect of shoot rearing on silkworm cocoon crop performance. Silkworm rearing can be of two types: one in which leaf is plucked from the tree and then fed to the worms whole or cut as the growth of the silkworms demand. In other, the entire branches can be used generally after IV moult. There has been considerable controversy on shoot rearing (Anonymous, 1945; Krishnaswami et al., 1973; Malvazzi et al., 1974). Some are of the opinion that shoot rearing causes under nourishment and ultimately leads to more number of unequals (Ali, 1952). If the plantations are away from the rearing house it would be difficult to transport branches than the leaf detached from the branches. It is also evident that shoot rearing saves labour costs which constitutes a major expenditure in silkworm rearing (Krishnaswami et al., 1973).

In case of leaf feeding the leaves were plucked from the trees and preserved in leaf chamber (Krishnaswami et al., 1973) and fed to silkworm adlibitum. But in shoot rearing the shoots were harvested from the field and transported to rearing house and thick ends of branches were inserted in to a bed of sand of 10cm thickness and kept moist by watering it frequently. The shoots were placed one against the other to form a sort of triangular arch and also against wall. Whole shoots were supplied in each feeding from IV moult onwards. Optimal rearing conditions were adopted during the rearing (Krishnaswami, 1978). At the time of spinning detached leaf was served to both batches.

In shoot rearing, larval duration during Vth instar was reduced by 7.95% ($P < 0.001$). There was no significant difference in weight of silk glands, 10 mature larvae, cocoon, shell and shell percentage. 18 kg leaf quantity was required to produce 1 kg of cocoons under shoot rearing while, in the leaf feeding, it required 22 kg. There was no significant difference in the effective rate of survival between two treatments. Leaf consumption and man hours required for Vth instar rearing was reduced drastically in shoot rearing when compared to leaf feeding ($P < 0.001$).

Rearing on shoots permits a saving in the labour on collection of leaf, distribution of feeds, bed changing and spacing. Thus, a rearer who practices the shoot rearing in Vth instar saves 34% of his time which could be utilized on other jobs. It also helps further in economizing labour since pruning is also done simultaneously. In the leaf feeding method the worms crawl on the leaf. Spoil it and often refuse to eat it. Such rejections increase the litter which is 25% of the total weight of the feeds. But in shoot rearing the worms crawl on the branches and therefore do not spoil the leaf which they consume to the last morsel. In addition to this leaf on shoots remain fresh for a longer periods which is advantageous over leaf plucked from shoots. Necessity for bed changing is reduced to the minimum and the space required also reduced by one third. The hygienic conditions that prevails in shoot rearing such as cleanliness, aeration, fresh food, optional spacing helps to improve quality and quantity of cocoons.

The analysis of the data did not showed any significant differences in cocoon characteristics between leaf feeding and shoot rearing. All other things were equal, the leaf and labour consumption was less which was advantageous over leaf feeding. Shoot rearing not only decreased the leaf cocoon ratio but also saved the labour considerably, and brought down the cost of production of cocoons. In the present study shoot feeding was adopted in all experimental rearing farms. However, many other farmers adopted leaf plucking method. It is necessary to popularize shoot feeding concept on large scale not only in southern Maharashtra but also in other parts of the state. The shoot feeding method was found quite economical over leaf plucking method in southern Maharashtra.

Vindhya *et al.* (1996) made analysis and comparison of shoot and stand rearing of silkworm *B. mori*. The growth rate of sericulture has increased by about 10% per annum over the past decade in India (Sinha, 1990 and Thomas, 1990). Commercial production of cocoon occupied a place of pride in the rural economy of our country. It was estimated that about 60% of the cost goes to the raising and maintenance of mulberry garden and 40% to the silkworm rearing (Rangaswami *et al.*, 1976; Ullal & Narasimhanna, 1978). According to Benchamin and Jolly (1987) the cost of cocoon production was 42.87 percent and out of it 76.2 percent goes towards the labour costs. Since the cocoon contributes roughly 80 percent of the cost of raw silk production it is essential to produce the same at minimum cost. Ali (1952), Krishnaswamy (1973) and Ganesh (1978) advocated shoot rearing method as it requires lesser labour component which constitute a major expenditure on silkworm rearing. Japanese scientists Tazima (1972) and Omura (1980) also favoured the shoot rearing methods of silkworm rearing. Similarly, in India also some authors like Narsimhamurthy and Subramanyam (1989) Shekharappa *et al.* (1991) reported that shoot feeding in rack system was more economical method.

Dar and Singh (1996) studied the comparative performance of silkworm *B. mori* under three feed versus traditional four feed rearing schedule. Investigations on the performance of silkworms

B. mori reared under three feed traditional four feed rearing schedule, were carried out in Kashmir valley in three rearing seasons, spring, summer and autumn. The experiment included six treatments, the feeding time was variable in each treatment. The best performance in terms of larval weight, cocoon weight, shell weight and shell ratio was higher under the treatment with feeding schedule as 6 a.m. 1 p.m. as compared to control (6 a.m., 10 a.m., 4 p.m. and 9 p.m.). The three-feed system with feeding time at 10 a.m.

Rapusas and Gabriel (1976) have made an investigation on the optimum ecological conditions of silkworm rearing or silk production. The results suggest that the performance of silkworm was always better in all respects such as growth, survival, mortality, disease incidence, silk yield and fecundity, when reared in large rearing bed at comparatively low densities even under the different ecological intima and the amount of space available to each larva appeared to be more important than the amount of food per larva.

Ngarmprasit *et al.* (1987) conducted an experiment based on three rearing seat space such as 3, 4, 5 mt^2 per 5000 larvae in three silkworm rearing periods and came to the conclusion that seat space of 5 mt^2 box gives the best results. The findings indicated that wider spacing was helpful to improve the rearing performance of silkworm.

Roychoudhury *et al.* (1990) have clarified unequivocally the role of crowded, optimum and wider larval rearing space as indicated by Japanese, Indian and Chinese spacing schedules for rearing of bivoltine silkworms, during adverse and favourable climatic conditions. Development has been found to be accelerated there by reducing the larval duration in larvae reared under wider spacing. The wider spacing played a positive and significant (P<0.05) role in improving growth and most of the parameters of rearing performance including reeling details and reproductive potentiality [Roychoudhury *et al.*, 1991]. Crowded conditions prolonged larval stage, cause high mortality and induced detrimental effects on growth, cocoon characters and reproductive performance. Population density has been found to play an important role in physiological programming of larvae in relation to rearing space. Further differential response of spacing schedules in unfavourable and favourable seasons exhibited the interactions between climatic and physiological factors, and the possible relationship between spacing and rearing performance can not be excluded as irrelevant. Thus, authors have made recommendations to use wider spacing for bulk commercial bivoltine rearing.

Roychoudhury *et al.* (1991) further conducted an experiment based on the population density made of 5, 10, 20, 40, 80, 160 and 320 larvae under constant rearing space of 187 sq. inches during the last stage larvae of bivoltine silkworm. Results revealed that the larval density of 40 larvae followed by 80 larvae show maximum improvement of growth and cocoon characters, but no significant ($p < 0.05$) difference has been found between the two populations. On this basis, the optimum space requirement of bivoltine silkworm has been found to be 2.33 sq.inches/larva.

Sengupta and Yusuf (1978) studied effect of spacing during rearing on different larval and cocoon characters on some multivoltine breeds of silkworm *B. mori*. A detailed study of the space requirement of some evolved multivoltine breeds of silkworm (DI4b, D3C, MBDV), *B. mori*, indicated a direct effect of larger spacing towards the improvement of larval and cocoon characters like wt. of 10 mature larvae, yield per 10,000 larvae brushed (No. & Wt.), cocoon wt., shell wt. and absolute silk content. In trays of 2½' × 2' the character progressively improved with the number of larvae from 400 down to 100, though in general the groups 100-200 behaved much better. This trend in many cases existed upto 300 worms per tray. On this basis the requirement of space per 100 dfls reared (30,000 larvae after 4th moult) comes to about 500 sq. ft. This being based on cellular rearing, a spacing two-third of it or 300-350 sq. ft. per 100 dfls. has been recommended for bulk commercial rearing. It is established that lesser the number of worms in a particular space, the better are its individual characters. The limit of maximum rearing for worm having a larval weight of 2.0 to 2.5 gm, without any significant detrimental effect appears to be round about 300 worms per tray of 5 ft. Taking about 30,000 worms per 100 dfls in the 5th stage, the approximate space requirement would be about 500 sq.ft. However, this being calculated at the cellular level and the requirement in mass beds being considered to be appreciably lower (Masui, *op. cit.*, Tanaka *op. cit.*), a spacing up to two-third or 300 to 350 sq. ft. per 100 dfls. may be considered to be adequate for commercial rearing.

Sivaprakasan *et al.* (1997) studied the influence of spacing on the incidence of grasserie in silkworm, *B. mori*. They reported that grasserie incidence significantly increased when the larval density in the rearing tray increased. The larval mortality at Vth instar due to grasserie was maximum (51.4%) at the population level of 7000, 3500, 1750 and 875 larvae for second, third, fourth and fifth instars respectively (8662 cm²) and was minimum (11.4%) at the population levels of 437, 218, 109 and 55 larvae for second, third, fourth and fifth instars respectively (8662 cm²). Stress produced by crowding, malnutrition and other environmental factors had been reported to increase the susceptibility of insects to diseases (Steinhaus, 1958; Vago, 1959). Crowding as a stress has been used to bring out latent diseases (Helms and Rawn, 1971). In the present study spacing adopted was 70-72 sq. ft. for third instar, 100-105 sq. ft. for fourth instar and 220 -225 sq. ft. for fifth instar.

In silkworm rearing, time is an important factor as for as mounting is concerned. If mounting method is unsuitable, the quality of cocoon will be affected and cause financial loss to the farmer. Hence, the period from mounting to completion of spinning is considered important as it would affect the cocoon quality and overall silk grade. Though, the labour requirement for mounting is only about 10% of the total labour required for silkworm rearing, it is said to be a skilful task. During mounting, more than anything else, high temperature and high humidity adversely affect the reeling quality of cocoons. In recent days, rotary mountages recommended by the Japan International Co-operation Agency (JICA) are being popularized for bivoltine rearing in the states of Karnataka, Andhra Pradesh and Tamil Nadu for improvement of cocoon and silk quality. These rotary mountages help the farmers to get cocoons of better shape, size and quality and are fastly becoming popular.

The cocoon formation by silkworm needs appropriate environmental conditions and type of mountage. There are different types of mountages used for spinning of silkworms viz., bamboo mountages, collapsible plastic mountages etc. In the practices of mounting, storage of bamboo mountages occupies a lot of space and improper handling may cause contamination of rearing house. Keeping the trays with the collapsible mountages renders inadequate aeration and results in poor cocoon formation.

There is also a chance of damage to worms due to falling and contamination of the rearing premises. These practices are poorly protected against uzi-fly infestation and a considerable portion of cocoons will be lost.

Singh and Rajan (2001) reported that urination was usually completed within one day after mounting. About 40 cc urine was discharged by 100 mature worms at the time of mounting. All the urinated mat or paper etc. should be removed as early as possible. Therefore, sufficient ventilation and aeration must be provided. During mounting, mature silkworm starts looking for a suitable site for spinning and then settles down at selected place for spinning. After some time when a thin layer of cocoon has been formed, the silkworm sticksout its tail region outside the cocoon and does it last defecation followed by urination. Only after this, silkworm enters the main cocooning stages. Although, the spinning continues without pause however, if the silkworm is disturbed by any physical means or exposed to sudden violent environmental change, it sometimes stops spinning. This causes for poor reeling. Singh and Rajan (2001) also reported that forty rotary mountages are required to mount silkworms of 100 dfls. Cost of one set of rotary mountage was estimated around Rs. 500 and the cocoons harvested from such mountage fetch Rs. 20 to 30 more when compared to bamboo chandrikes due to better quality.

Srinivasababu et al. (2002) investigated viable mounting platform for quality seed cocoon generation. In Basic Seed Farms, generally two or more races will be reared at a time. In the present practice of mounting, there is a possibility of mixing of breeds, disease contamination, uzi-fly infestation and also improper or poor formation of cocoons affecting the pupation rate. The spinning of silkworm demands, $23 \pm 1°C$ temperature and humidity of 60 to 70% with gentle flow of air in the mounting room. These conditions help in good pupation resulting in high egg recovery. There had been various innovations on mounting and materials used for mountage. However, in spite of many improvements, a few drawbacks are common. A low cost viable mounting platform was devised using locally available materials by Srinivasababu et al. (2002) and also a technology for mountage suitable for basic seed farms was developed at Basic seed farm, Gavimata, K.R. Pet, Karnataka. Srinivasababu et al. (2002) utilized the cost of new mounting which they investigated as 77.50 rupees. They also visualized advantages of their new mountage as follows -

1. Easy to store and occupies less space, cost effective, maintenance free, long lasting and consumes less labour for mounting compared to other mounting materials.

2. The disinfection of platform is very easy and consumes less disinfectant as compared to other mountages.

3. The platform gives good aeration which is essential during the spinning stage.

4. The moisture loss during cocooning period is very important which determines the pupation rate. The same is ensured during mounting on the viable mounting plantform.

In present study plastic mountages made by CSR & TI, Mysore have been adopted in rearing of silkworms by selected farmers. However, other farmers used indigenous material such as coconut fronds, red gram sticks, mulberry sticks and other locally available sticks with encouraging results.

Our experience shows that summer months of March, April and May were not favourable for silk-worm rearing. This was one season when most of the things go wrong against the desirability of successful rearing management. Crop failures were common. Feed quality of the mulberry was poor, food consumption was low and larval growth was sluggish resulting in poor cocoon crop of low weight and silk content. Sericulturists thus face the problems of high risk of failure and low return, forcing them to believe that avoiding summer crop is the best possible step. However, there are measures that can be adopted to minimize the risk and assure better silkworm rearing requirement and scientific management. Silkworm is poilkilothermic animal and its body temperature changes in relation to the environmental temperature. All physiological functions are influenced by environmental temperature. Silkworms are capable of growing in temperature range of 15° to 40°C. The ideal temperature for physiological activities ranged from 20°C to 28°C.

Humidity also plays a vital role in silkworm rearing. The effect of humidity was both direct and indirect. Humidity directly influence the physiological functions of the silkworm such as ingestion, digestion, pH value of the blood and CO_2 expiration. The indirect effects are the rate of drying of leaves, its suitability as a feed and consumption etc., The requirement of temperature and humidity for silkworm differs from age to age. Young age larvae (I, II and III age) are more resistant to high temperature and humidity and grow healthier in such conditions. Late age larvae (IV and V age) grow more healthier in low temperature and humidity environment. Considering the importance of temperature and humidity the silkworm rearers should pay more attention for artificial adjustment of temperature and humidity to create most favourable climatic conditions for successful cocoon crop harvest (Shivakumar, 1993).

In the hotter regions, rearing house is constructed under shade providing cross ventilation, sufficient windows, false roofing. During summer season, the young age silkworms are provided with paraffin paper, wet foam pads, rearing box and are fed with fresh leaves with more moisture content. During the late age rearing, the temperature is maintained with wet clothes for doors and windows, humidifier, bed covered with paraffin paper, and sand beds below the rearing stands, cool air is allowed inside the rearing room during night times by keeping the windows opened.

During cooler season, young age silkworms were reared without foam pads and paraffin paper. Room heater/charcoal stove was used to increase the temperature. Use of lime in the rearing house and for rearing beds during moulting, feeding smaller size leaves, less quantity of feeding to avoid the use of moist leaves etc. were practised (Shivakumar 1993). The present study was conducted in Southern Maharashtra geographically and climatically different, and results are in accordance with the principles stated by the earlier workers (Benchamin, 1997 and Shivakumar et al., 1993). Climatically, Solapur is hot district, its temperature range is 39°C to 45°C in summer and most of the farmers stop the silkworm rearing in those month. However, irrigated farmers continue in the crop harvesting in the season. It was observed that the incidence of diseases like flacherie and grasserie was too high in Solapur district and comparatively the incidence of grasserie and flacherie was low in Kolhapur district in summer and was moderate in Sangli district. Solapur is hot district of southern Maharashtra.

Shivakumar *et al.* (1995) reported that sericulture was intensively practised in southern and eastern states of India as a traditional culture and recently, some of the non-traditional states (northern, western and central parts) have also taken up sericulture. The summer season (March-June) in these areas was characterized by high temperature (30°C to 40°C) and low humidity; while the silkworms grow well between 22° to 28°C temperature and 75 to 85% humidity. Because of high temperature and low humidity in these regions, the health and growth of the silkworms were adversely affected resulting in out break of diseases like grasserie and flacherie in total or partial crop failure. Manipulation of temperature and humidity was of prime importance to create favourable environment during silkworm rearing. In tropical region, management of these two factors became a major problem in different seasons.

Mengl (1980) reported that the province of Jammu has its typical non-mulberry sericulture region extending from Pathankote in the South to Banihal in the north, and from Duda to Poonch in east-west direction. The sericulture area was sub-divided into 22-rearing zones. As many as 12,000 families inhabiting 1240 villages in these 22 zones get engaged with silkworm rearing as the spring sets out its smile in this rugged terrain. On an average 12,000 ounce of seeds were distributed in these zones. The work of seed distribution starts in early February and continues upto the 3rd week of April.

The spring season sets in usually on the 7th of February in Jammu. Accordingly, the first appearance of buds on the branches of mulberry was noticed on the very first day. It has been generally seen that, prior to this day also, the sprouting in the mulberry farms and in the field was quite perceptible. The cycle of climate has undergone so much of mutation that the sericulture operations are often affected by the abrupt rise and fall in temperature. The results indicate that the rearing in Jammu area can be anticipated with the advantage of warding off the perils of early sprouting and high temperature at the late stage. For the first time in the sericulture history of Jammu, the traditional races, at the level of grand parents and first filial generation, were processed before the usual time of rearing giving the results. This unfolds the promise of over-coming such eventualities.

Muniraju (2001) studied pure Mysore (multivoltine) and NB_4D_2 (bivoltine) silkworm races and reared at constant temperatures of 26, 28, 30 and 32°C during young age. Combinations of above temperatures were employed during late age rearing. The results revealed that combination of lower temperature during young age and higher temperature at the late age was found better than constant high temperature regions throughout the larval period. However, it was confirmed that higher temperature (upto 30°C) during young age followed by relatively lower temperature (<26°C) at the late age was found ideal.

Radha Krishna (2001) revealed that the fecundity of traditional race was significantly high during winter and rainy seasons. The total and the fifth age larval durations were significantly low during all the seasons in both new races and their hybrids. The pure breeds and hybrids of the new races had shown significantly higher values for cocoon yield by number and weight during winter and rainy seasons than that of the traditional race. Single cocoon weight showed highly significant variation in the new hybrids during all the seasons and was nonsignificant during summer in the pure races. However, the shell ratio has not shown significant improvement in the new breeds. Further, the pupation ratio in both pure breeds and hybrids of the new races was found to be significantly higher during all the seasons than that of the traditional race. The filament length (814 cm); denier (2.06) and reliability (90%) in NLP x NB_4D_2 were higher than that of the Pure Mysore x NB_4D_2 (749 m, 2.04 and 88% respectively), whereas, the filament length in NLZ x NB_4D_2 (682m) was less than that of pure Mysore x NB_4D_2.

Nutrition plays a vital role in determining the health and productivity of the silkworm, B. mori. The quality of the leaf is reported to depend upon the tenderness, succulence and high nutrient contents in the leaf (Benchamin and Nagaraj, 1987). Moreover, the nutrient contents of mulberry leaf in turn are known to very depending on the season, agronomical inputs, type of harvesting and storing of the leaf (Chaun and Chaung, 1988; Sarkar et al., 1992). Further, the leaf silk ratio has close correlation with the health condition of the silkworm (Ding et al., 1991). Hence the quality of leaf decides the quality of silk (Horie, 1976; Krishnaswami, 1978; Chaun and Chaung, 1988; Lee et al., 1991; Aruga, 1994).

Basvarajappa and Savanurmath (1997) studied the influence of stored leaves on incidence of larval grasserie and cocoon characters of silkworm, *B. mori*, in Northern Karnataka, India. They reported that the susceptibility to the grasserie disease and the per cent cocoon moulting enhanced due to the feeding of leaves which were stored for more than 18h. The NB18 and its hybrid Pm x NB 18 were relatively more susceptible to the grasserie when fed on stored leaves. The bivoltines appeared more sensitive even for shorter duration of storage i.e. for 12h. Hence, the incidence increased in direct proportion to the longer duration of storage. Further there was a significant difference existed between the silkworm breeds and the stored leaves. In general, the larval duration prolonged on feeding the stored leaves. The effect was observed only in leaves which were stored for 18 h and beyond. Comparatively, the NB18 appeared more sensitive than NB_4D_2 and the Pm x NB18. Where as, the mature worm weight decreased in all the silkworm breeds on feeding leaves which were stored for more than 24h. However, such effect was observed in NB_4D_2, fed 12 h stored leaves and the Pm x NB18, fed 18 h stored leaves.

Per cent cocoon formation decreased in direct proportion to the storage of the leaves. The Pmx NB18 recorded low per cent cocoon formation (75.5%) as compared with other breeds. Interestingly, the leaves for 24h increased the cocoon weight. But the shell weight decreased in direct proportion with the duration of the strong. While there existed a considerable difference between the shell weight of bivoltine (NB 18 and NB_4D_2) and the cross-breed (Pm x NB18) at the normal conditions, the silkworm breeds maintained on stored leaves have hardly indicated any difference. The shell ratio decreased at the duration of leaf storage increased. In bivoltines, it was remarkably lowered. The ERR by number and weight did indicate a proportionate decrease when the stored leaves were fed. However, there was no significant statistically variation. NB_4D_2 breed was very sensitive to feeding on 6h stored leaves, but the increase in ERR by weight on feeding the 12h stored leaves gradually decreased along with the increase in the duration of storage. The estimated cocoon yield of NB18 and its hybrid Pm × NB18 was poor when fed on leaves stored beyond 12h. Comparatively the NB_4D_2 recorded good cocoon yield. In the present study only Pm × NB_4D_2 was tried and the results are more economic in Solapur district.

Vijay Kumari *et al.* (2001) studied the effect of feed cut in fifth instar on cocoon characters and disease incidence in silkworm *B. mori*. Newly evolved productive bivoltine silkworm hybrid CSR2 × CSRS rearing was conducted by them with different levels of feed cut (10, 20, 30, 40%) during the 5th instar. The rearing performance and disease incidence was recorded. The result indicated that the cocoon characters were deteriorated and susceptibility to disease incidence was increased with the increase in feed cut. All the rearing parameters were significantly improved and disease incidence was reduced, with optimum feed.

Sing *et al.* (1989) studied the relative susceptibility of different breeds of silkworm (*B. mori*) to diseases under natural conditions. They made the observation on the breeds in winter, summer and rainy season. Their results indicated that on an average the recorded ERR in multivoltine races was 93.61%, 91.33% and 90.78% in Pm, *C. nichi* and MYI respectively. NB_4D_2 recorded the least yield (78%) followed by NB7 (78.6%), NB18 (79.39%) and PCN (88%). The yield component was higher in multivoltine races as compared to bivoltines. There was a significant difference in the incidence of diseases between the races. Higher incidence of diseases were recorded in bivoltine races as compared to multivoltine races. On an average 10.89%, 10.44%, 12.05%, 2.34%, 2.06%, 2.78% and 1.39% incidence of grasserie was recorded in NB7, NB18, NB_4D_2, PCN, PM, *C. nichi* and MYI races respectively. Highest incidence of flacherie was recorded in NB, (10.44%) followed by NB18 (10.17%), NB_4D_2 (9.95%) and PCN (9.60%). Minimum occurrence of flacherie was recorded in Pm (4.33%) followed by *C. nichi* (5.89%) and MYI (7.83%). The trend was almost similar i.e. bivoltine races exhibited highest disease occurrences and multivoltines recorded minimum incidence of diseases during all the three seasons. In the present study bivoltine races are not tried. There is need to work on bivoltine races in Maharashtra. Our results indicated that muscardine incidence was more in Kolhapur than Solapur and Sangli and grasserie and flacherie was more in Solapur, only in summer season.

The silkworm, *B. mori* is an economically important insect, is affected by several diseases. Grasserie, perbrine, white muscardine and bacterial flacherie are commonly prevalent diseases caused by different pathogens viz., Nuclear polyhedrosis virus, *Nosema bombycis, Beaureria bassiana* and different types of bacteria including *Bacillus thuringiensis.* About 34-40% of the total crop in a year is lost due to diseases in India (Vaidya, 1960). However, with the advent of improved silkworm rearing technology, cocoon production has increased in recent years but still there is about 15-20% crop loss due to diseases (Baig and Pradeep Kumar, 1987). As there are no curative measures, these diseases are best prevented through proper disinfection of rearing house and appliances, sterilization of larval surface and rearing bed by application of various bed disinfectants. Several authors have tested different disinfectants viz. phenolic compounds (Hegna, 1977), sodium hypochlorite and formalin (Vail *et al.,* 1968) and formalin (lgnoffo and Garcia, 1968) against several pathogens. Various disinfectants viz. formalin (Kagawa, 1980), asiphor (Venkata Reddy *et al.,* 1990) and chlorinated lime and hydrochloric acid (Miyasima, 1979) were tested against silkworm pathogens. Formalin is a commonly used disinfectant in all the sericultural tracks of India for disinfection of rearing house and appliances. But it is suitable for rearing house where airtight facilities are available and is not suitable for open and dwelling type of rearing houses. It also causes inconvenience to the residents by its pungent and irritating odour. Under these circumstances, an alternate disinfectant which can be more suitable to Indian sericulturists without any health hazards is an urgent need.

Balavenkatasubbaiah *et al.* (1994) tested the bleaching powder in different concentration was tested against the pathogens of silkworm, *B. mori; Nuclear polyhedrosis virus, Beauveria bassiana, Nosema bombycis* and *Bacillus thuringiensis.* The results were compared with that of formalin which is the commonly used disinfectant. All the concentrations of bleaching powder tested were found significantly effective in the inactivation of nuclear polyhedra of NPV, conidia of *B. bassiana,* spores of *N. bombycis* and *B. thuringiensis.* Bleaching powder in 4 and 5% were found to be more effective than 2% formalin.

Subbarao *et al.* (1992) used bleaching powder solution (5% W/N) as spray for disinfection before rearing silkworm and during the course of rearing, lime and lime-bleaching powder mixture (97:3) dusted once daily as bed disinfectant on grasserie and muscardine inoculated silkworms and lime-bleaching powder effectively inactivated the NPV and increased the survival of silkworm upto 16.6 and 17.5% respectively over control. Similarly, lime-bleaching powder increased the survival by 20.75% over control in the muscardine infected population.

Devaiah *et al.* (1982-83) observed that first instar silkworms were more susceptible than second instar when inoculated with spores of *A. flavus*. Mortality of the worms increased with the increase in the spore density, significant differences existed amongst the various fungicidal treatments. Among the three experimental fungicides pafsol was least effective. Kabinoran was the best fungicide followed by kinuban on both first and second instars.

Jadhav *et al.* (2000) studied the low cost rearing method for *B. mori*, (Pm × NB$_4$D$_2$) by adopting indigenous shelves in Maharashtra. Their results indicated that the cost of rearing equipments averaged Rs. 583.40 (range Rs. 432 to 840) with sarrie shelves which was considerably less than the standard method, Rs. 6000 while, the shelves prepared by Nylon mesh and fertilizer bags cost averaged Rs. 959.30 and Rs. 756.40 respectively. The cocoon yield is ranged from 40 to 61 kg. with an average of 43.15 kg. per 100 dfls while, selling price ranged from Rs. 110 to 137 an average of Rs. 128.90 per kg. of cocoons produced. The net amount saved towards investment of rearing equipments with nylon, old cotton sarries shelves per 100 dfls averaged Rs. 5316.60 (range Rs. 4502 to 5568) while, the income generated per 100 dfls averaged Rs. 5646.90 (range Rs. 3330 to 8537). The man power required averaged 24.4 mandays (range 22 to 27 mandays). The above results indicate that the shelves prepared by nylon/old cotton sarries were more economical than the other shelves and has great relevance in sericulutral practices and further, for upgrading the socio-economic status of the people of Marathwada, specially, poor and marginal community of farmers. The initial investment is quite low and feasible to adopt by poor farmers. The quality of cocoons produced was very satisfactory since rendita was 9.2.

Jadhav *et al.* (1998) also exploited china type rearing method for late age silkworm *B. mori*, (Pm × NB$_4$D$_2$) in dwelling in Maharashtra. The bamboo racks of size 11' × 3.25' × 6' were prepared by using bamboo rods and bamboo mattress of size 5' × 3'. The rods were burried in the ground at the depth of half feet. The lengthwise distance between two rods 5.5 feet and widthwise distance was 3.25 feet. On each rod nails of the size 12 cm long and 1 cm in diameter were fitted, at a distance of half feet. After preparing skeleton, out of rods, the bamboo mattresses were kept over the nails at one feet. Thus, 24 mattresses of 5' × 3' were adjusted. This created sufficient space for rearing of 100 dfls. For easy feeding and cleaning shelves can be brought down by adjusting shelves on nails at a distance of half feet. After feeding, shelves can be arranged over alternate nails so that, sufficient space is provided for good ariation to silkworms. At this stage good ariation is required for healthy growth of silkworms. Total investment for shelves and rods averaged Rs. 588.00 only. The rendita (10-11) of the crop was not affected. The experiments were conducted in villages, Hiwara, Judgaon and Vahegaon of Aurangabad district. 20 farmers were selected for conducting the study. During the rearing, the worms were fed four times. The cleaning was practised twice in fourth and fifth stages. On an average the temperature and humidity conditions were 24°-26°C and 70-75% respectively at rearing places. For feeding purpose leaves of Kanva-2 variety of mulberry were utilized. The functioning age of this devise was same as noted in standard equipments. The above results indicate that, the proposed method *i.e.* China type rearing method has great relevance in sericulture for increasing the living standard of farmers specially, poor and marginal ones. In the present study the selected farmers were adopted the low cost rearing technique proposed by Jadhav *et al.* (2000) and found quite encouraging. In the present study rendita was also considered for the assessment of rearing performance and cocoon production in three districts of southern Maharashtra. The average rendita for Solapur was 9.01, for Sangli 9.04, and Kolhapur 9.87. The results indicated that rendita was not affected significantly in three districts.

Jadhav *et al.* (2001) studied the role of metrological components in sericulture development in Nagpur Maharashtra (Vidarbha region). Their results showed that cocoon yield per 100 dfls, consumption of dfls/acre, cocoon production etc. were influenced mostly, by environmental factors, (temperature, humidity and rainfall). Highest plantation of mulberry 157 acres with 140 farmers recorded during 1999-2000. However, higher consumption of dfls 188/acre during 1998 and lest 101 dfls/acre during 2000, yield of cocoons, 19.76 kg/100 dfls as a highest and 16.52 kg/100 dfls lowest were recorded during 1999-2000 and 1998-99 respectively. Maximum cocoon production in Nagpur district, 2612 kg was recorded during 1999-2000. The temperature, humidity and rainfall played critical role in development of sericulture in Nagpur.

Jadhav *et al.* (2002a) studied paired row system of mulberry cultivation in Maharashtra. They reported that rainfall plays a very crucial role in determining the productivity of mulberry leaves. Paired row system of mulberry cultivation (2'×1') X 6' found most suitable against traditional (3'×3') method of cultivation in water tress conditions for sustainable sericulture development in Maharashtra. In the present study, same spacing of mulberry plantation was adopted and results were quite encouraging.

Jadhav *et al.* (2002b) also studied the impact assessment of transfer of technologies in sericulture entrepreneurship at Hiwara village, Aurangabad district (Maharashtra). They reported that sericulture is a agrobased industry, highly suitable to the rural poor farmers and weaker sections of the society. Sericulture in the state is likely to gather momentum. It is the only cash crop which provides frequent attractive returns throughout the year. Transfer of technologies (TOT) is imperative for deriving optimum benefits by farmers. Intensive extensive efforts are needed in the dissemination of new technologies in a given time. Acceptance of new techniques by the farmers is comparatively slow mainly due to socio-economic situation. Krishi Vigyan Kendra and District Sericulture Office, Department of Sericulture, Aurangabad took up TOT programme on sericulture in identified villages in Aurangabad district.

Hiwara in Aurangabad district was selected for sericulture entrepreneurship and TOT programme. The village falls under dry agroclimatic zone with medium to light soils. Mulberry gardens were predominantly of M-5 variety with paired row system of cultivation. Individual interactions and group discussions were held regularly to motivate the farmers. Silkworm rearing were conducted in the dwelling places/simple thatched huts. Low cost silkworm rearing methods were introduced for successful cocoon harvests. The area under mulberry had increased with improvement in cocoon productivity. Money flow through cocoon sales also improved to the overall development of the village. Dissemination of knowledge in sericulture technologies to the neighbouring villages and districts was also encouraging. Southern Maharashtra has a tremendous potential in sericulture business as it is connected with sericulturally developed states, Karnataka and Andhra Pradesh. Transfer of technology in sericulture would worth hoping maximum yield of cocoons and the data will serve as basis for standardizing the rearing method of silkworms and transfer of technology in the region.

6

CONCLUSION

Sericulture is an important agroforest based industry earning a foreign exchange of Rs. 2235.38 crores/ annum (year 2001-2002) and providing gainful employment to over 7 million people. India has the distinction of being bestowed by nature with all the commercial known varieties of silk viz. mulberry, tasar, eri and muga. The overall mulberry silk production of the country for the year 2001-2002 was 15845 mt. Besides raw silk, India produces annually about 588 tons of spun silk yarn and 262 tons of noil yarn. Estimated production of mulberry silk waste was around 5255 mt during the year 2001-2. Silk reeling capacity in India consists of about 35490 charkas and 25979 flature/cottage basins. Raw silk is invariably twisted in small factories for use in handlooms and powerlooms. There are over two hundred thousand twisting spindles in India. About 60% of Indian silk is now estimated to be woven on handlooms and 40% on powerlooms. The provisional export earning from silk goods during the year 2001-02 is decreased to Rs. 2235.38 crores (7.7%) as compared to 2000-01 which was 2421.98 crores. There is always a demand-supply gap of about 5000 mt of raw silk. The above account clearly indicates that there is a tremendous scope for sericulture in India.

The share of Maharashtra in sericulture is very negligible. Hence, there is a scope to do for sericulture in Maharashtra and need to boost sericultural activities in the state. Specially, the districts, Kolhapur, Sangli and Solapur of southern Maharashtra have a great importance in sericulture business, since these three well suited for sericultural practices climatically and secondly, bounded southewordly by Karnataka and Andhra Pradesh, sericulturally well developed states. These districts can obtain benefits of transfer of technology from these states and have good opportunities of marketing and several types of other interactions in sericulture business.

In the present work, silkworm rearing technique has been assessed with respect to abiotic and biotic factors in Kolhapur, Sangli and Solapur districts of southern Maharashtra. These districts were selected for the present study as they have special attributes with respect to geography and climate. Kolhapur have high rainfall and low temperature, Sangli moderate rainfall and temperature while Solapur shows low rainfall and high temperature.

During the course of study (years 2000 to 2002) it has been observed that the number of cocoons produced per 100 dfls was highest in Solapur district moderate in Sangli district and lowest in Kolhapur district. The same sequence was noticed with per kg. cocoon weight and cocoon grades. It has been also observed that the incidence of grasserie, flacherie and muscardine diseases were very common in all 3 districts of southern Maharashtra. However, in Solapur district incidence of diseases was very low, specially in rainy and winter seasons, it was moderate in Sangli and highest in Kolhapur district. In general, incidence of grasserie or flacherie was noticed from March and peaked in the month of July in all the districts. Muscardine incidence was noticed from November and peaked in February and then declined. The incidence of Grasserie in summer was highest in Solapur district, it was moderate in Sangli and lowest in Kolhapur district. The incidence of flacherie was also highest in Solapur district and moderate in Sangli and lowest in Kolhapur. However, the incidence of muscardine was highest in Kolahpur district, moderate in Sangli and lowest in Solapur.

From pests, only uzi-fly *Exorista bombycis* Lois was the major menace in all 3 districts. Uzi-fly incidence was noticed throughout the year at different rearing centres of three districts. However, its population peaked in February and June during the year. Incidence of uzi-fly was highest in Kolhapur district, moderate in Sangli and lowest in Solapur district. It has been observed that uzi-fly incidence was not found on rainfed crops of Solapur district but it was noticed on the irrigated crops of sericulture. In Kolhapur and Sangli districts, uzi-fly is well established. Infact, in Kolhapur district, it caused severe losses to crops (62%).

On the basis of results obtained it can be concluded that in districts Kolhapur, Sangli and Solapur of southern Maharashtra sericulture can be practised satisfactorily. Infact, though rainfall is low and temperature is high, Solapur districts is leading and most suited for sericulture. However, crop harvestation number is less in Solapur because of water scarcity and high temperature in summer.

The incidence of muscardine and uzi was very common in Kolhapur district. Uzi caused 62% losses to crops in Kolhapur district. Incidence of pests and diseases may be the cause of reduced sericultural activities in Kolhapur district in addition to the attractive cash crops such as sugarcane and grapes in the region. However, Sangli is emerging slowly but steadily as a sericultural district in Maharashtra. Overall, the present work will be helpful for guiding the sericultural practices and uplifting the farmers socio-economic standard in the region.

7

SUMMARY

Sericulture is an important agroforest based industry and good source of earning foreign exchange and providing gainful employment. India has the distinction of being bestowed by nature with all the commercial known varieties of silk viz. mulberry, tasar, eri and muga. India ranks 2nd in the world by producing 15845 mt. row silk during the year 2001 to 2002. There is always demand supply gap of about 5000 mt. of raw silk. The above account clearly indicates that there is a tremendous scope for sericulture in India. The share of Maharashtra in sericulture is very negligible. Hence, there is scope to do for sericulture in Maharashtra. In Maharashtra Kolhapur, Sangli and Solapur (Southern Maharashtra) are the leading districts in sericultural practices. These districts are vary climatically and geographically and bounded (Southwordly) by Karnataka and Andhra Pradesh, sericulturly well developed states. These districts can obtain benefits of transfer of technology from above states and have good opportunities of marketing and several kinds of interactions in sericulture business. In the present study, silkworm (*Bombyx mori* L., Pm x NB$_4$D$_2$) cocoon production have been assessed with respect to biotic and abiotic factors in three districts of southern Maharashtra namely Kolhapur, Sangli and Solapur.

The book has been divided into eight chapters.

The first chapter includes the general introduction containing national and international status of the subject and advances in research.

The second chapter is devoted for rearing of silkworm *B. mori*.

The third chapter deals with shoot feeding for silkworm rearing.

The fourth chapter contains ecology of rearing of *B. mori*. During the course of study (years 2000 to 2002) it has been observed that the number of cocoons produced per 100 dfls was highest in Solapur district, moderate in Sangli and lowest in Kolhapur. The same sequence was noticed with per kg. cocoon weight and cocoon grades. It has been also observed that the incidence of Grasserie, Flacherie and Muscardine diseases was very common in all 3 districts of Southern Maharashtra. However, in Solapur district incidence of diseases was very low specially in rainy and winter seasons, it was moderate in Sangli and highest in Kolhapur district. In general, Grasserie and Flacherie incidence was noticed from March and peaked in the month of July in all the districts. Muscardine incidence was noticed from November and peaked in February and then declined. It was highest in Kolhapur, moderate in Sangli and lowest in Solapur. The incidence of Grasserie in summer was highest in Solapur district, it was moderate in Sangli and lowest in Kolhapur district. The incidence of Flacherie was also highest in Solapur district and moderate in Sangli and lowest in Kolhapur.

From pests, only Uzi-fly *Exorista bombycis* Louis was the major menace in all 3 districts. Uzi-fly incidence was noticed throughout the year at different rearing centres of three districts. However, its population peaked in February and June during the year. Incidence of uzi-fly was highest in Kolhapur district, moderate in Sangli and lowest in Solapur district. It has been observed that uzi-fly incidence was not found on rainfed crops of Solapur district but noticed on the irrigated crops. In Kolhapur and Sangli districts, uzi-fly is well established. Infact, in Kolhapur district, it caused severe losses to crops (62%).

The fifth chapter embodies different trends adopted for rearing *B. mori* under which earlier findings have been compared with the present work. The chapter also explores several avenues for future research.

The sixth chapter deals with the conclusion on the present findings. On the basis of results obtained it can be concluded that in all three districts, Kolhapur, Sangli and Solapur of Southern Maharashtra, sericulture can be practised satisfactorly. Though rainfall is low and temperature is high, Solapur district is leading and most suited for sericulture. However, crop harvestation number is less in Solapur because of water scarcity and high temperature in summer.

The incidence of Muscardine and uzi was very common in Kolhapur district. Uzi caused 62% losses to crops in Kolhapur district. Pests and diseases may be the cause of reduced sericultural activities in Kolhapur district in addition to the attractive cash crops such as sugarcane and grapes. However, Sangli is emerging slowly but steadily as a sericultural district in Maharashtra. Overall, the present work will be helpful for guiding the sericultural practices and uplifting the farmer's socio economic status in the region.

The seventh chapter represents the summery of the book and the eighth chapter includes bibliography referred.

BIBLIOGRAPHY

Aher, A.A., Kamate, I.A. and Sohany, G.G. 1994. Sericulture extension in non-traditional areas : the Baif experience. *In Int. Conf. Seric. Global-silk- scenario-2001*, CSRTI, Mysore, 25-29 Oct 1994, 45.

Ahsan, M.M, Dhar, A., Dhar, K.L. and Fotedar, R.K. 1990. Package of practices for mulberry cultivation under temperature conditions. *Indian Silk*, 29(2), 7-12.

Ali, H. 1952. Silkworm rearing, Department of Sericulture, Kashmir.

Ananthanarayana, S.R., Kasthuribai, A.R. and Chandrashekaran, M.K. 1978. Effect of light and darkness on the behaviour of *B. mori. Indian J. Exp. Biol.*, 16, 922-924.

Anil Kumar, K.H. 1992. Disinfection of the rearing house. *Indian Text, J.* 103(1), 134.

Anonymous, 1945. Silkworm Rearing on Branches. *Research bulletin No. 2*, Sericulture Research Station. Ales, France.

Anonymous, 1973. Annual report of the central sericultural research station, Berhampore (West Bengal), 1972-73.

Anonymous, 1987. Biochemical evaluation of leaf quality of K2 mulberry variety under two systems of pruning. Central Sericultural Research Training Institute. Annual Report, 28-29.

Armstrong, V. 1989. "Sericulture for Adivasis in Nilgiris." *Workshop on Sericulture Extension and Management* (Central Sericultural Research and Training Institute, Mysore) 30-31 August, 1989.

Aruga, H. 1994. Principles of sericulture (Translated from Japanese). Publ. by Mohan Primlani for Oxford & IBH Publ. Co. Pvt. Ltd., New Delhi.

Ayuthaya, N. 1972. The host preference of the tachinid fly to different stages and varieties of silkworm. *Bull Thai Sericult. Res. Train. Centre*, 2, 67-69.

Ayuzawa, C., Sekido, D., Yamakawa, K., Sakurai, U., Kurato, W., Yaginuma Y. and Takoro, 1972. Hand book of silkworm rearing. *Fuji pub. Co., Ltd.*, Tokyo, Japan, p. 319.

Balavenkatasubbaiah, M.R.K. Datta, M. Baig, B. Nataraju and M.N.S. Iyengar 1994. "Efficacy of bleaching powder as a disinfectant against the pathogens of silkworm, *Bombyx mori* L". *Indian J. Seric.*, 33, 23-26.

Bari, M.A., Islam, R. and Salam, M.A. 1985. Feeding effects of 3 mulberry varieties on nistari races of silkworm (*Bombyx mori*). *Bangladesh J. Zool*, 13(1), 13-18.

Basavarajappa, S., and Savanurmath, C.J. 1996. Effect of different mulberry varieties during late-age silkworm, *B. mori* on incidence of grasserie and the cocoon characters. *Uttar Pradesh J. Zool.*, 16(2), 104-108.

Beeson, C.F.C. and Chatterjee, S.N. 1935. The biolosy of Tachinidae (Diptera). *Indian Forest Recods*, 1, p. 184.

Benchamin, K.V. 1922. Chawki Silkworm rearing an evaluation. *Indian silk.*, 18,20.

Benchamin, K.V. 1993. Sericulture in Bangladesh. *Indian Silk.* 32 (6), 17-21.

Benchamin, K.V. and Jolly, M.S., 1987a. Employment and income generation in the rural areas through Sericulture. *Indian silk*, 25, 9-13.

Benchamin, K.V. and K.V. Anantharaman, 1990. Standardisation of Moulting Test" to evaluate mulberry leaf quality under tropical conditions. *Indian J. Seric*, 19(2), 255-62.

Benchamin, K.V. and Jolly M.S. 1987b. Sericulture, Economics, A hand book for sericulture extension workers, C.S.R. & T.I. Mysore.

Benchamin, K.V. Gapuz, J.V. and Jayaramaraju, P. 1998. Influence of photoperiod on emergence, fecundity and fertility in multivoltine breeds of silworm, *B. mori. Indian J. Seric*, 29, 110-118.

Benchamin, K.V. and Krishnaswamy, S. 1981. Studies on the egg production efficiency in silkworm, *B. mori*. on the various factors contributing to egg production. *Proc. Seric. Symp.* Seminar TNAV, Coimbatore, 1-6.

Benchamin, K.V. and Nagaraj, C.S. 1987a. Silkworm rearing techniques. In: Appropriate sericulture techniques, M.S. Jolly (Ed.), International Centre for Training and Research in Tropical Sericultue, Mysore, India. 69-90.

Benchamin, K.V. and Nagaraj, C.S. 1987b. Silkworm Rearing techniques, (Ed.) Manjeeth S. Jolly. *Appro. Seri. Tech.* 64-106.

Bendgude, H.G., Khanvilkar, V.G. and Dalvi, C.S. 1987. Relative performance of three pure races of mullberry silkworm. *Indian J. Seric,* 26(1), 54-56.

Bhat, D.V. Noamani, M.K.R., Pillai, S.V., Nagaraj, C.S. and Ramamohan Rao, 1989. Preliminary assessment of four popular bivoltine breeds of silkworm, *Bombyx mori L. Indian J. Seric,* 28(2), 261-262.

Bhide, S. 1994. Sericulture in Andhra Pradesh by 2001, Souvenir, International Conference on Sericulture : Global Silk Scenario 2001, 125-129.

Boedts, B. 1990. The practices of tropical sericulture in Karnataka State, South India. *Tropicultura,* 8(2), 94-98.

Bongale, U.D. 1991. Mulberry sericulture zones and agro-climate in Karnataka. *Indian Silk,* 30(5), 7-12.

Bose, P.C. 1992. Reducing the cost of cultivation of mulberry. *Indian Silk* 30(12), 44-45.

Chandrasekhar, M. and Thangavelu, K. 1988. Soil amelioration techniques for mulberry cultivatioin. *Indian Silk,* 27(6), 13-17.

Chaun, W.P. and Chaung, C.D. 1998. Silkworm rearing (Translated by Chen, Z.P., Zhzhng, L.P. & Tang. He. RSTC. Guanghou, China) *FAO Agri. Service Bull,* UNO Rome, 73(2), 39-56.

Chikkanna, Aanjaneya Gowda, D.D., Singhvi, N.R. Srinivas, G., Iyengar, M.N.S. and Datta, R.K. 1995. Study on adoption of behaviour of Sericulturists and their characteristics in Kolar district of Karnataka. *Indian J. Seric,* 34(1), 10-14.

Chikkanna, Singhvi, N.R., Kulkarni, V.S., Subramanian R.K., Sen, A.K., Iyengar, M.N. and Datta, R.K. 1993. Impact of Chawki rearing on crop performance. *Indian Silk,* 32(7), 34-36.

Choudhury, P.C., Shukla, P., Ghosh, A., Malikarjuna, B. and Sengupta, K. 1991. Effect of spacing crown height and method of pruning on mulberry leaf yield, quality and cocoon yield. *Indian J. Seric*, 30(1), 46-53.

Dandin, S.B. 1994a. Women in sericulture : Development issues. *Indian Silk*, 33(5) : 15-20.

Dandin, S.B. 1994b. Corporate sectors involvement in seri business. In Int. Conf. Seric. Global silk-scenario-2001, CSRTI, Mysore, 25-29 Oct 1994, pp. 49.

Dandin, S.B. 1987. Problems and Prospects of mulberry cultivation in Malnad region. *Indian Silk*, 25(9), 19-24.

Dandin, S.B. 2002. Factor oriented approach and resource management for productivity and quality improvement in sericulture. *Proc. XIXth Cong. Intnat. Seri. Comm.*, Bangkok Thailand, 1, 423-441.

Dandin, S.B. and Ramesh, S.R. 1987. A kalpa vruksha called mulberry. *Indian Silk*, 26, 49-53.

Dandin, S.B. and Sarkar, 2002. Mulberry varietal improvement in India. *Proc. XIXth Cong. Intnat. Seri. Comm.*, Bangkok, Thailand, 1, 23-32.

Dar, H.U. and Singh T.P. 1996. Comparative performance of silkworm *B. mori* under three feed versus traditional four feed rearing schedule. *J. Seric*, 4(1), 15-19.

Das, Gupta, Abhijit, 1994. Sericulture in Karnataka by 2001. Souvenir, International Conference on Sericulture. Global Silk Scenario 2001, 121-124.

Das, B.C. and A.K. Sikdar. 1970. Evaluation of some improved strains of mulberry by feeding experiment. *Indian J. Seric*, 9,1.

Das, P.K., Choudhary, P.C., Ghosh, A., Katiyar, R.S., Mathur, V.B. and Datta R.K. 1993. Use of Azotobacter biofertilizer in mulberry cultivation. *Indian Silk*, 31,43.

Das, P.K., P.C. Choudhury, A. Ghosh, B. Malikarjuna, N. Suryanarayana and K. Senguta, 1990. Effect of green manuring dry weed and black polythene mulching on soil moisture conservation, growth and yield of mulberry and their economics under rainfed conditions. *Indian J. Seric*, 29(1), 263-272.

Das, P.K., Ghosh, A., Choudhruy, P.C., Katiyar, R.S. and Sengupta K. 1992. Responses of irrigated mulberry to Azotobacter and Azospirillum biofertilizer under graded levels of nitrogen in biofertilizer technology transfer (L.V. Gangawane, Edu). *Associated Publishing Company*, New Delhi, 714.

Das, P.K. and K. Vijayaraghavan 1990. Studies on the effect of different mulberry varieties and seasons on the larval development and cocoon characters of silkworm, *Bombyx mori (L). Indian. J. Seric* 19, 44-53.

Das, P.K. and Vijayaraghavan K. 1990. Studies on the effect of different mulberry varieties and seasons on the larval development and cocoon characters of silkworm *B. mori. Indian J. Seric*, 29(1), 44-53.

Datta, R.K. 1992. Guidelines for Bivoltine Rearing. Central Silk Board, Bangalore, India, 83.

Datta, R.K. 1994. Need for involvement of corporate sectors in quality silk production. In Int. Conf. Seric. "Global-silk-scenario-2001, CSRTI, Mysore, 25-29 Oct 1994, 50-51.

Datta, R.K. 1995. Sericulture biotechnology. *Proc. Nat. Acad. Sci. India*, (B), II (suppl.) 201-216.

Devaiah, M.C., Kawakami, K. and Govindan, R. 1982-83. Efficacy of some fungicides on the control of aspergillus disease of the silkworm, *B mori. Indian J. Seric*, 21 (2), 73-74.

Dhanorkar, B.K., Jawale, M.D., Tayade, D.S. and Unchegaonkar, P.K. 1992. Effect of variety-cum-spacing on leaf yeild of mulberry under Marathwada conditions. In Nat. Conf. *Mulberry Seric. Res.* CSRTI. Mysore, Dec. 10-11, 41-42.

Ding, N., Zhang, X.M. Jiang, M.G., Xu, W.G., Wang, Z.E. and Xu, M.K. 1991. Studies on the dietary efficiency of the silkworm, *B. mori* on the physiological factors of the leaf silk ratio. *Canye kexue*, 17 . 193-199.

Dolli, S.S., Kalppa, H.K., Subramaniam, R.K., Chikkanna, Singhvi, N.R., Sen, A.K., Lyengar, M.N.S. and Datta, R.K. 1992. Extent of adoption of improved sericultural practice by the sericulturists. *In Nat. Conf. Mul. Seric, Res.* CSRTI, Mysore, Dec. 10-11, 41-42.

Fugo, H. Iwata, Y. and Nakajima, M. 1984. Eclosion hormone activity in haemolymph of eclosing silkworm, *B. mori. J. Insect Physiol.*, 30, 471-475.

Ganesh, N.K. 1978. Indo-Mauritious Silk Bonds. *Indian Silk*, 17(6), 101-105.

Gangwar, S.K., Somasundaram, P. and Thangavelu, K. 1993. Feeding behaviour of silkworm, *Bombyx mori*. *J.Adv. Zool.* 14(2), 115-118.

Gayathri Devi, K.G. 1994. Karanataka : A status report on women in sericulture. *Indian Silk*, 32, 31-38.

Griridhar, K., N. Sivarami Reddy and K. Satya Prasad. 1991. Volumetric studies in bivoltine silkworm (*Bombyx mori L.*) breeds reared on different mulberry (*Morus sp.*) varieties. *Indian J. Seric*, 30(1), 135-37.

Gopal, S. 1994. NABARD and the development of sericulture. *Indian Silk*, 33 (6), 21-23.

Gopinath, G.R. 1994. Scope for large scale farming in sericulture in India. In Int. Conf. Seric." Global silk scenario - 2001", CSRTI, Mysore, 25-29 Oct, 89-92.

Govindaiah, Sharma, D.D., Bajpai, A.K. and Datta, R.K. 1997. Mulberry cultivation in China. *Indian Silk*, 36, 41-46.

Govindan, R., Magadum, S.B., Bheemanna, C., Narayanaswamy, T.K. and Ashoka, J. 1992. Influence of mulberry varieties on larval silk gland cocoon and cocoon shell weight in silkworm, *Bombyx mori L. PKV (Punjabrao Krishi Vidhyapeeth) Res. J.*, 16(1), 30-33.

Gupta, B.K. and Sen, S.K. 1989. Identification and management of contributing factors of cocoon in field. Workshop on Sericulture Extension and Management (Central Sericultural Research and Training Institute, Mysore) 30-31 August, 1989.

Harcharan, Singh and Mavi, G.S. 1986. Rearing of mulberry silkworm (*Bombyx mori L.*) during autumn and spring seasons under the Punjab conditions. *J. Entomol. Res.*, 10(1), 79-84.

Hassanein, M.H. & El. Shaarawy, M.F. 1962. The nutritional value of certain mulberry varieties - Revue DUVER A SOIE - Journal of Silkworm, T.IV. XIV.

Hegdekar, A.P., B.M. and Batsch, W.W. 1972. A chemically defined synthetic medium that induces oviposition in the parasite *Itoplectis conguisitor. Can. Ent.*, 96, 1030-34.

Helms, T.J. and Rawn, E.S. 1971. Perennial laboratory culture of disease free insects. In : Microbial control of insects and Mites, H.D. Burges and Hussey (Eds.), Academic Press, New York, 639-654.

Himantharaj, M.T., Kamble, C.K., Rajan, R.K. and Datta, R.K. 1994. Silkworm rearing house construction : an ideal approach. *Indian Silk*, 33(4), 19-22.

Hiromu, A. 1998. Global scenario of wild silks. *Indian silk*, 37, 18-20.

Horie, Y. 1976. Qualitative study as food utilization by silkworm *B. mori* through its life cycle. 1. Economy of dry matter, energy, carbon. *J. Seri. Sci. Japan*, 41, 175-180.

Iwata, E. 1978. On the study of primary prunning to train low cutting mulberry plants. *Bull. Seric. Expt. Stn. (Tokyo)*, 27, 397-426.

Iwata, E. 1981. Studies on the growth of regenerated shoot after intermediate prunning and its application to cutivation of mulberry. *Bull. Seric. Expt. Stn. (Tokyo)*, 28, 393-398.

Jadhav, A.D., R.S. Akare and T.V. Sathe, 2001. Role of metrological conditions in sericulture development in Nagpur - MS. XVIth *National Convention on major thems, Multidimentional impact of physics in agriculture* - IAPT, Yavatmal 23-25th Nov., 2001.

Jadhav, A.D. Sathe, T.V. Kamadi, N.G. and Undale, J.P. 2000. Low cost rearing method for *B. mori*. (Pm X NB_4D_2) by adopting indigenous shelves. Environmental issues and sustainable development, Vinit publ. Aurangabad, pp. 81-82.

Jadhav, A.D., Kamadi N.S., Sathe T.V. and Rode S.A. 2001a. Silk industry of Maharashtra - A perspective Nat. Semi. *Mulberry Sericulture Research in India,* - KSSR & DI, Bangalore, 26-28th Nov., 2001, p.148.

Jadhav, A.D., Sathe T.V. and Undale J.P. 1988. Exploitation of China type rearing method for late age silkworms *(B. mori L.) J. Seric*, 6 (1 and 2), 53-54.

Jadhav, A.D., Salunkhe, D.Y., Sathe, T.V. and Kamadi, N.G. 2000. Development of sericulture in Kolhapur district of Maharashtra. *Nat. Conf. Strategies for Sericulture R & D*, Mysore, 2000.

Jadhav, A.D., Kamadi, N.G., Akre, R.S., Nadre, K.R. and Sathe, T.V. 2002. Paired row system of mulberry cultivation a new approach in sericulture for drought situation. *Proc. Sem. Drought and water Resources IWRS*, Nagpur, April, 16.

Jadhav, A.D., Nadre, K.R., Kambadi, N.G., Sathe, T.V. and Rode, S.A. 2002. Impact assessment of transfer of technologies in sericulture entrepreneurship at Hiwara Village, Aurangabad district (Maharashtra). Marathwada Agricultural University, Parbhani - 431402. *Nat. Sem. Entre. Devpt. in Agri.*, March 2-3, 2002.

Jawale, M.D. and Tayade, D.S. 1987. Effect of bed disinfectants. *Sericologia*, 27 (3), 443-446.

Jameson, A.P. 1992. Report on the diseases of silkworms in India. Govt. printing, India, International books and periodicals supply service, New Delhi, India, pp. 62-64.

Jayaswal, K.P. and Raut, S.K. 2000. Influence of low temperature incubation on diapause incidence and quantitative traits in *B. mori, Utter Pradesh J. Zool*, 20(3), 233-237.

Jelmoni, E. (1943). Growing mulberries in reduced form (as shrubs etc.) Italian Agriculture, 80, 197-204.

Jingade, A.H., Vijayalakshmi Rao and Samson, M.V. 2000. Hatching pattern and embryonic growth of the pigmented eggs in the non-diapausing multivoltine race, pure Mysore, of the silkworm, *B. mori. Geobios*, 27(2-3), 73-76.

Jolly, M.S. 1967. A brief report on wild sericigena in India with special reference to Tasar culture. World Meet Silk product, Mauiracia pp. 1-6.

Jolly, M.S. 1986. Development and promotion of sericulture in India. Nat. Semi. on prospects and problems of sericulture in India. March 27-30.

Jolly, M.S. 1987. Chawki rearing-concept, organization and management. *Indian Silk*, 25 (9), 32-37.

Jolly, M.S. 1998. Oak Tasar in India : Problems and prospects. *Indian Silk*, 37, 35-37.

Kale, V.C., Pawar, D.S., Rajmane, K.D. and Nagarogoje, S.R. 1993. Economics of sericulture in Parbhani district of Maharashtra. *J. Maharashtra Agric. Univ.*, 18(3), 438-441.

Kamble, C.K. 1988. Effect of cold storage on hatchability of cross breed and acid treated bivoltine eggs of silkworm, *B.mori*. *Uttar Pradesh J. Zool*, 18(1), 37-43.

Kanyadi, N.M. 1989. Sericulture in the hill areas of Karnataka; encouraging past, bright future. *Indian Silk* 28(3), 23-26.

Kasiviswanathan, K., Pavankumar, T., Chaudhary, P.C. and Somashekara Reddy, K.S. 1988. How to grow mulberry in tropical countries. *Indian Text. J.*, 98 (7), 73-80.

Katti, S.R., Venkatesh, H., Puttaswamy, S. and Raghuraman, R. 2001. Seasonal variation in fecundity and hatching in some popular races of *B. mori*. *Geobios*, 28(4), 205-208.

Kaul, H.N. 1990. Indian's silk industry-current status and future scope. *Text magazine*, 31 (11), 33-35.

Kirsur, M.V. 2001. Along the silkroute, *Indian silk*, January 24-25.

Koul, O, Tikoo B.L, Saxena, P. and Atal, C.K. 1979. Growth and silk production in *Bombyx mori* L. fed on three different varieties of mulberry. *Jammu Tawi*, 18(1).

Koundinya, P.R. 1987a. "What can be done to boost sericulture in Gujarat?" *Indian Silk*, 26(4), 28.

Koundinya, PR. 1987b. Sericulture in Surat district. *Indian Silk* 25(10), 37-39.

Krishna, Rao, J.V., Singh, R.N. and Singh, C.M. 1998. Tribal development and wild silks. *Indian silk*, 37, 79-83.

Krishnaswami, S. 1978a. New technology of silkworm rearing CSR & TI Mysore. Bull. No.3, 1-10.

Krishnaswami, S. 1978b. New technology of silkworm rearing II. *Indian Silk.*, 17, 17-21.

Krishnaswami, S. 1978c. New technology of silkworm rearing. CSR & TI, Mysore, 2, 1-23.

Krishnaswami, S 1980. Improved method of rearing young-age (chawki) silkworm-I. *Indian silk*, 11(17).

Krishnaswami, S. 1986. Maintenance of parental silkworm races in commercial productiion of silkworm seeds. *Indian silk*, August, 5-8.

Krishnaswami, S. 1993. Special features of tropical sericulture and five crucial steps to successful silkworm rearing. *Indian Silk*, 13(9), 27-34.

Krishnaswami, S. and Venkataram, K. 1991. Sericulture research in India and its impact on sericulture development. *Sericologia* 31(1), 217-221.

Krishnaswami, S., Jolly, M.S., and Datta, R.K. 1964. A study on the fly pest infestation of the larvae and cocoon of *Bombyx mori L. Indian J. Seric*, 3, 7-12.

Krishnaswami, S., K.R. Noamani and M. Asan, 1970. Studies on the quality of mulberry leaves and silkworm cocoon crop production. *Inidan J. Seric.* 9(1).

Krishnaswami, S.S., Kumararaj, K., Vijayaraghavan and K. Kasiviswanathan, 1971. Silkworm feeding trails for evaluating the quality of mulberry leaves as influenced by variety, spacing and nitrogen fertilization. *Indian J. Seric*, 10(1).

Krishnaswami, S., Narasimhanna, M.N., Suryanarayana, S.K. and Kamaraj, S., 1973. *Manual on sericulture*, 2 silkworm rearing. FAO. *Agri Service Bull*, 15, 131.

Kumararaj, S.K. Vijayaraghavan and S.Krishnaswamy, 1972. An experiment aimed at enriching the mulberry leaf feed with 2 percent solutions of casein jaggery and urea for inducing better growth of silkworms and thereby to improve the yields and quality of cocoon crops was carried out. *Indian J. Seric*, 11 (1).

Kumaraswami, B.K. Basappa Reddy, M. and Jayakumar, M.J. 1992. Mulberry for dry lands of Karnataka. *Indian Silk*, 31(6), 5-10.

Kusiwar, E. 1989. Growth and leaf production of muberry (Morus nigra) pure and mixed with soybean and peanut. *Bul. Penelitian Hutan*, (510), 1-8.

Lakshmanan, S. and Thiagarajan, V. 1991a. Growth of mulberry silk output in India-component analysis. *Agric. Sit. India* 46(9), 651-654.

Lakshmanan, S. and Thigarajan, V. 1991b. (CSR & TI, mysore). Grown of Indian silk export - an analytical approach. *Agr. Sit. India*, 46(2), 87-89.

Lee, W.C., Kwon, Y.H., Kim, K.S., Choi, J.H., Lee, J.H., Kim, D.I., Kim, H.J., Rho, K.W., Lee, D.O. and Lee, S.W. 1991. Effect of several livestock excrement on the leaf yield and quality of mulberry (alba). *Res. Rep. Rural. Der. Adm. Suweon*, 33, 17-19.

Lombardi, Da, P.L. 1960. Attuale Stato Della Gelsicoltura Italiana Sestemazonie per eventuali allevamenti Successivei Con Pigerimento anche Al Tipi Giapponesi Importati 'eme Conference Technique Sericicole International Murice Avril Rev. DUVER-A SOIET. I. Vol. XII. Lou, Y. 1993. A technique model of cultivating and rearing suitable for the flood bed mulberry field to produce 100, 200 kilograms of cocoons. Peru. *Bull. Seric*, 24(1), 23-26.

Louis, J.A.M. 1980. A few words on the present state and future prospects of sericulture in Bengal. Civil service printing and publishing Co. Ltd., London, P. 31.

Malvazzi, A. Areus, O.C., Desouza, C.F. and Maria Oueiroz, L. 1974. Silkworm larvae *B. mori.* with entire and catted up mulberry tree leaves *Morus alba., C.B. Industrial Anim* Sp. 31, 167-171.

Mani, M., Thontadarya, T.S. and Singh, S.P., 1987. Record of natural enemies on the grape mealy bug, *Maconellicoccus hirsutus* (Green). *Curr. Sci.*, 56, 624.

Manjunath, D., Kishore, R., Satya Prasad, K., Kumar, P. and Datta, R.K. 1992. Biology of mulberry mealy bug and predatory potential of its biocontrol agent. National Conference on Mulberry Sericulture Research, 10th December at CSR & TI, Mysore, p. 50.

Marihonnaiah, Y. 1987. Income and Employment Generation in Dryland Sericulture and Ragi Mixed Crop Enterprises in Kunigal Taluk, Tumkar District, Karnataka. Thesis of P.G. Degree in the Univ. of Agricultural Sciences, Bangalore.

Masui, 1929. Quoted by Tanaka in "Sericology", Central Silk Board, Bomby-2, India.

Mathur, A.P. and Mathur, J.P. 1992. Adoption of sericulture among tribals of South Rajasthan. In Nat. Conf. Mulberry Seric Res. CSR & TI, Mysore Dec. 10-11, 41-42.

Mathur, V.B., Rehman A., Geetha Devi and Rahmathulla A. 2000. Influence of environmental factors on spinning larvae and its impact on cocoon and reeling characters. *Abstracts National conference on strategies for sericulture research and development.*, pp. 69.

Matsumara, S. and Ishizuka, Y. 1929. The effect of temperature on the development of *Bombyx mori. Bull. Seric. Exp. Stn. Jpn.*, (19).

Meechuen, Jariya, 2002. Use of an evaporative pad cooling system in the growing process of grown silkworms. Proc. XIXIth Cong. Int. Nat. Seri. Comm., Bangkok, Thailand, 1, 536-538.

Meenal, A. Mathur, V.B. and Rajan, R.K. 1994. Role of light during incubation of silkworm eggs and its effect on rearing performance and diapause. *Indian J. Seric*, 33(2), 139-141.

Mengl, A.L. 1980. Makeshift rearing schedule to match climate mutation in Jammu. *Indian Silk*, 23-25.

Mishra, R.K., Choudhury, P.C., Ghosh, A., Singh, G.B. and Datta, R.K. 1992. Evolution of cultivation technology for mulberry garden for young age silkworm. In Nat Conf Mulberry Seric Res. CSRTI, Mysore Dec. 10-11, 41-42.

Mottghitlab, M. and Pourali, M. 2002. Some preliminary results from silkworm, *Bombyx mori*, reared whole instar on different artificial diets in Iran. *Proc. XIXth cong. Int. Nat. Seri. Comm., Bangkok*, Thailand, 1, 122-126.

Muniraju, E., Sekharappa, B.M. and Raghuraman, R.R. 2001a. Production potential of silkworm, *B. mori* under different rearing temperatures. *Indian J. Seric*, 40, 15-20.

Muniraju, E, Sekharappa, B.M. and Raghuraman, R. 2001b. Effect of delayed brushing of black-boxed eggs on hatching and rearing performance in silkworm, *Bombyx mori. L. Indian J. Seric.*, 40(1), 76-80.

Nagaraj, C.S., Geeta Devi, R.G. and Rathna Sen. 1989. Issue on rearing management and crop stability. Workshop on Sericulture Extension and Management (Central Sericultural Research and Training Institute, Mysore) (30-31 August, 1989).

Nahar, K.U., A.V. Dhuri and R.B. Dumbre. 1989. Performance of some hybrids of mulberry silkworm, *Bombyx mori L.* in Konkan. *Indian J. Seric*, 28 (2), 145-149.

Nair, N.V. 1988. Sericulture - its place in national economy, *Indian Silk*, 6, 22-24.

Narasimha, Murthy, C.V. and Subramanyam, K.V. 1988. Effect of shoot rearing on silkworm cocoon crop performance. *Indian J. Seric.*, 27(2), 156-158.

Narasimhamma, M.N. 1988. Manual on silkworm egg production. CSB, Bangalore.

Narasimhamurthy, C.V. and Subramanyam, K.V. 1989. Effect of shoot rearing on silkworm cocoon performance. *Ind. J. of Seri.*, 27(2), 156-158.

Narayanaprakash, R., Perisamy, K. and Radhakrishnan, S. 1985. Effect of dietery water content on food utilization and silk production in *B. mori*, (Lepidoptera : Bombycidae). *Indian J. Seri*, 24(1), 12-17.

Narayanan, E.S. and S.S. Chawla, 1965. Effect of frequency of feeding on the growth and development in two races of silkworm, local mysore and shungetsu hosho. *Indian J. Seri*, 4, 4.

Narayanan, E.S., K. Kasiviswanathan and M.N. Sitarama Iyengar, 1967. Preliminary observations on the effects of feeding leaves of varying maturity on the larval devlopment and cocoon characters of *Bombyx mori L. Indian J. Seric.*, 6, 2.

Noamani, M.K.R. and Pandey, R.K. 1992. Prospects of sericulture in the North-Eastern India. *Indian Silk*, 30 (12), 8-13.

Omura, S. 1980. Silkworm rearing technique in the tropics Japan International Co-operation Agency. Tokyo, Japan, 105, 124-129.

Paroda, R.S., 1993. Crop science research for sustainable agriculture in India. *Pro. Nat. Acad. Sci. India.* 63, 97-114.

Parthasarathy, V.S. and Gregory, S. 1994. NGOs Sericulture and Development. In Int. Conf. Seric. Global silk scenario - 2001, CSR & TI, Mysore 25-29 Oct 1994, 56-57.

Patil, G.M. and Visweswara Gowda, B.L. 1986. Micro-climatic manipulatin in silkworm rearing. *Reshme Krishi* 8(4), 29-34.

Paul, D.C. 1987. The employment potential of mulberry silk industry in North-East region of India. Seminar on prospect of mulberry sericulture in the Eastern Region of India 5/6 May Berhampore.

Pavan Kumar, T. 1989. Effective measures for the transfer of technology for maximum cocoon crop in different areas. Workshop on Sericulture Extension and Management Central Sericultural Research and Training Institute 30-31 August, 1989.

Pershad, G.D., Datta, R.K., Vijaykumar, H. V., Bhargava, S.K. and Jolly, M. S. 1986. Performance of some multivoltine races of *Bombyx mori. L. Sericologia*, 26(3), 295-301.

Radhakrishnan, S. and Periasamy, K. 1986. Studies on the selection and method of cultivation of mulberry. National Seminar on Prospects and Problems of Sericulture in India. March 27-30.

Radhakrishna, P.G. Sekharappa B.M. and Gururaj, G.S. 2001. Seasonal reponse of the new multi-bivoltine hybrids of the silkworm, *B. mori, Indian J. Seric*, 40(2), 174-176.

Rajshekhargouda, R. and Devaiah, M.C. 1983. Occurrence of uzi-fly, *Exorista sorbillans* Widemann (Diptera, Tachinidae) in Northern districts of Karnataka (Abstract), *Natl. Semi. Silk Res. Dev.*, Bangalore, p. 113.

Raju, P.J., Mahadevappa, R., Raghuraman and S.B. Dandin, 1995. Sericulture among tribals of B.R. Hills. *Indian Silk*, 34, 10-12.

Rangaswami, G. Narsimhama, M.N. Kashivishwanthem, Sastry, C.R. and Jolly M.S. 1976. Sericulture manual mulberry cultivation FAO Agri, Service Rome, Italy, Publish by C.S.B. Bangalore, India.

Rao, U.R. 1996. Presidential address. 83rd *Indian Science Congress, Patiala*, pp. 1-48.

Ray, Indrajit, 1989. Can mulberry provide an answer to the scourage of AIDS. *Indian Silk*, 27, 37-38.

Reddy, Y.G. 1992. Prospects of self-employment through sericulture. *Indian Silk*, 31(2), 5-8.

Reddy, D.N.R. and Kotikal, Y.K. 1988. Pests of mulberry and their management. *Indian Silk*, 3, 9-14.

Reese, J.C. and Beck, S.D. 1978. Inter-relationships of nutritional indices and dietary moisture in the black cutworm (*Aqrotis ypsilon*) digestive efficiency. *J. Insect Physiol.*, 24, 473-479.

Saraswat, R.P. and Shrivastava, A.K. 1988. Dhanora becomes a model sericultural village in Marathwada. *Indian Silk*, 26, 21-13.

Saridiporn, Chuprayoon, Subaan Sopha and Nappron Kongpum, 2002. Influence of temperature egg preservation at early development stages on hatching ability of multivoltine silkworm, *Bomyx moir* L. *Proc. XIXth Cong. Intant. Seri. Comm.,* Bangkok, Thailand, 143-148.

Sarkar, A.A., Quader, M.A. Rab, M.A. and Ahmed, S.V. 1992. Studies on the nutrient composition of some indigenous and exotic mulberry varieties. *Bull. Seri. Res.,* 3, 8-13.

Sastri, T.V.N. Reddy, T.C. and Nagabhushanam, T.D.J. 1987. Economics of size in sericulture industry in Chittor. *Indian Silk* 26(2), 45-46.

Sathe, T.V., 1998. Sericultural crop protection . Asawari Publication. pp. 1-130.

Sathe, T.V., 2002. Intrinsic rates of increase and interspecific relationships between *Meteorus dichomeridis* and *Meteorus spilosmae,* the larval parasitoids of mulberry pest, *Spilosoma obliqua. Proc. XIXth cong. -Int. Nat. Seri. Comm.,* Bangkok, Thailand, 1, 39-46.

Sathe, T.V. and Bhoje, P.M. 2000. Biological pest control DPH-Delhi, pp. 1-121.

Sathe, T.V. and Jadhav, A.D. 2001a. Sericulture and pest management. DPH -Delhi. pp. 1-197.

Sathe T.V. and Jadhav, A.D. 2001b. Host plant attractivity in a model, *Cotesia glomeratus - Bombyx mori.* -mulberry. *Sericologia,* 41 (3), 459-470.

Sathe, T.V. and Mulla, M.D., 1999. Insect pests of mulberry from Kolhapur, India. *Geobios new Reports,* 18, 73-74.

Sathe, T.V., Jadhav, A.D., Mulla, M.K. and Mohite, A.P. 1998. Life table statistics and intrinsic rate of increase in Wai-4 *Bombyx mori. Journal of Eco-Physiology,* 1(2), 45-48.

Sathe, T.V., Mulla, M.K., Arballi, Gajendra and Rupali Pawar, 1999. White fly - A new pest of mulberry. *Indian silk,* 37, 10.

Sato, M. 1968. On production structure and matter production in mulberry plants. *Acta Sericologia,* 67, 1-6.

Satyanarayana Raju, Ch., Chandrasekharaiah, Venugopala Pillai, S. and Sengupta, K. 1990. Mulberrry conquest of the queen of hills. *Indian Silk,* 28(10), 44-48.

Scriber, J.M. 1978. The effect of larval feeding specialization and plant growth form on the consumption and utilization of plant biomass and nitrogen. An ecologcal consideration. *Entomol, Exp. Appl.*, 24, 694-710.

Sengupta, K. 1989. Sericultural extension and rural development some challenging issues. Workshop on sericulture Extension and Management, Central Sericultural Research and Training Institute, Mysore, 30-31 August, 1989.

Sengupta, A. and Yusuf, M.R. 1974. Studies on the effect of spacing during rearing on different larval and cocoon characters of some multivoltine breeds of silkworm, *B. mori. Indian J. Seric,* 13, 11-16.

Sengupta, K.B.D. Singh and J.C. Mustafa, 1971. A study on the effect of time of harvest of mulberry leaf on silkworm (*Bombxy mori L.*) cocoon crop and cocoon quality. *Indian J. Seric,* 10(1).

Sengupta, K., Kumar, P., Baig M. and Govindaiah P. 1990. Handbook on diseases and pests of silkworm and mulberry. *United Nations, ESCAP,* Bangkok, Thailand, pp. 35.

Sengupta, K.D. Ray, B.D. Singh and S. Krishnaswamy, 1972. Studies involving high dose nitrogen fertilization. *Indian J. Seric,* 12(1).

Sengupta, S., Mukherjee S.K., Sikdar A.K., Mustafa J.C., and Sengupta, D. 1973. A co-ordinated study on the effect of variety, spacing in cutivation and levels of nitrogen fertilization of mulberry on the cocoon yield and cocoon characters of multivoltine silkworm, *Bombyx mori L. Indian J. Seric,* 12 (1), 39-45.

Sharma, D.C. 1987. Sericulture development in Rajasthan. *Indian Silk,* 25, 8-9-10.

Shekharappa, B.M., Gururaj, G.S. Raghurama and Dandin S.B. 1991. Shoot feding for late age silkworm. KSSDI, Bangalore.

Shetty, K.K. and Samson, M.V. 1998. Non-mulberry sericulture in India. *Indian Silk,* 37, 21-25.

Shivakumar, G.R., Madhava Rao, Y.R. Himantharaj, M.T. and Datta, R.K. 1993. A single deveice to maintain temperature and humidity in rearing house. *Indian Silk,* 32(8), 45-46.

Shivakumar, G.R., Himantharaj, M.T., Magadum, S.B., Giridhar, K. and Datta, R.K. (1995). Management of silkworm rearing in summer. *Indian Silk,* 33(12), 13-17.

Siddappaji, C., Vasundhara, M. and Shandara, A.G. 1987. Friend evaluation of mulberry silkworm races in Karnataka. *Indian Silk*, 25(11), 30-35 and 38.

Siddhu, N.S., Sreenivasan and Shamachary, R. 1967. Fertility performance of female moths depends on their male mates. *Indian J. Seric.*, 6, 77-82.

Siddiqui, A.A., 1988. Tasar culture and its role in community development. *Indian Silk*, 26, 35-37.

Siddiqui, A.A. and Omkar, 1987. Impact of B.S.M. & T on tribal upliftment. *Indian Silk*, 25, 21-22.

Sigmatsu, H. and Takeshita, H. 1967. On the growth of silk glands and silk proteins production by silkworm reared at various temperatures during the fifth instar. *Acta Sericologia*, 65, 125-128.

Singh, K.P., Das, P.K. 1996. Some records of pests and predators of primary muga food plants and silkworms *A. assama* W. in Assam. *Sericologia*, 36, 763-765.

Singh, K.P. and Ghosh, P.L. 1992. Mulberry cultivation under agro-forestry and land management. *Indian Silk*, 31, 16-18.

Singh, G.B. and Rajan, R.K. 2001. Correct usage of rotary mountage. *Indian Silk*, pp. 5-8.

Singh, A. and Sadhu, A.N. 1986. Agricultural problems in India. Jammu University, Jammu, p. 386.

Singh, I. and Thangavelu, K. 1992. Co-operatives for the development of sericulture. *Indian Silk*, 30(12), 30-31.

Singh, Deo, S.N., Tribhuwan, Singh and Mamoni, Das, 1992. Performance of four popular bivoltine breeds of mulberry silkworm, *Bombyx mori L.* in Koraput. *Indian J. Seric*, 31(1), 61-62.

Singh, B.D., Baig, M., Balavenkatasubbaiah, M., Sharma, S.D., Sengupta, K. and Sivarami Reddy, N. 1989. Studies on the relative susceptibility of different breeds of silkworm (*B. mori*) to diseases under natural conditions. *Indian J. Seric*, 29(1), 142-144.

Sinha, S. 1990. The developement of Indian silk oxford and IBH publishing Co. Pvt. Ltd. 6 Janpath, New Delhi, pp. 16-17.

Sinha, S.S. 1994. (CTRTI, Ranchi). Role of non-government organizations in sericulture development. In Int. Conf. Seric. Global silk scenario-2001, CSR & TI, Mysore, 25-29 Oct 1994, p. 47.

Sivarami, Reddy, N. and Sasira Babu, K. 1990. Hatching patterns in the silkworm, *B. mori*, (Pm × NB_4D_2) under different photoperiodic combinations. *Proc. Ind. Acad. Sci. (Anim. Sci)*, 99(4), 327-334.

Sivarami, Reddy N. 1993. Implications of photoperiod on the silkworm, *Bombyx mori L.* (Pm X NB_4D_2). Ph. D. Thesis, Sri Venkateswara University, Tirupathi, India.

Sivarami, Reddy, N., Sasira Babu, K. and Pavankumar, T. 1984. Oscillatory frequencies in *B. mori*. (Pm X NB_4D_2). *Sericologia*, 24(4), 525-545.

Sivarami, Reddy, N., Shankar Naik, S. and Murali Mohan, P. 1998. Hatching patterns of silkworm, *B. mori*. as influenced by light intensity. *Indian J. Seric,* 37(2), 166-122.

Skopik, S.D. and Pittendrigh, C.S. 1967. Circadian systems II. The oscillation in the individual Drosophila pupa; its dependence of developmental stage. *Proc. Nat. Acad. Sci. USA*, 58, 1862-1869.

Sonwalkar, T.N. and Lakshmipathaiah, B.N. 1989. Marketing of cocoons and reeling. Workshop on Sericulture Extesion and Management, Central Sericultural Research and Training Institute, Mysore, 30-31 August, 1989.

Sree Kumar, S., Nair Sudhakaran, G., Appaswamy, P., Vijayaraghavan, K. and V. Thiagarajan. 1994. Now, mulberry on your dining table. *Indian Silk,* 32, 45.

Sriharan , T.P., Samson, M.V., Krishnaswami, S. and Datta, R.K. 1971. Laboratory investigations on uzifly, *Tricholyga bombycis* Beck., a tachinid parasite of silkworm (*Bombyx mori* L.): Rearing and reproduction of the parasite. *Indian J. Seric*, 10, 4-22.

Srinivasababu, G.K., Parthasarthy, B.A. and MurtazaBaig, 2002. Viable mounting platform for quality seed cocoon generation. *Indian Silk*, pp. 5-8.

Srinivasan, E.B. 1986. Mobile Soil Testing for Mulberry Gardens. *Indian Silk*, 25(5), 7-9.

Steinhaus, E.A. 1958. Stress as a factor in insect diseases. *Proc. Tenth Int. Congr. Entomol.*, 4, 725-730.

Subba Rao, G., Chandra A.K. and Bhattacharaya, J. 1992. Effect of bleaching powder and lime against grasserie and muscardine disease of the silkworm, *B.mori. Indian J. Seric.*, 31(1), 37-39.

Subba Rao, G., Chakravorty, N.G., Nath, S. Nath, T.N., Shamsuddin, M. and Sen, S.K. 1987. Scope of the bivoltine rearing in the district of Jalpaiguri (West Bengal). Seminar on Prospects of mulberry sericulture in the Eastern Region of India 5/6 May, 1987, Berhampur.

Subbarao, G., Mathur, S.K., Pramanick, D.R. and Sen. S.K. 1987. Interrelationship of ovaluation, oviposition and retention of eggs in silkmoth, *B. mori*. Effect of seasonal temperature and humidity. Seminar on prospects of mulberry sericulture in the Eastern region of India, Berhampur.

Subbu, Rathinam K.M., and J. Sulochana Chetty, 1991. Effect of fortification of mulberry leaves with minerals to silkworm, *Bombyx mori. L. Indian J. Seric.* 30(1), 121-123.

Sudhakaran, M. and Nagaraj, B. 1989. Sericulture in Kerala is vibrant and confident. *Indian Silk*, 28 (3), 27-31.

Suryanarayana, N., Dayananda Reddy, R. and Leeladevi, G. 1989. Transfer of Technology through training. Workshop on Sericulture Extension and Management, Central Sericultural Research and Training Institute, Mysore, 30-31 August, 1989.

Swaminathan, M.S. 1994. Biotechnology and fighting the fatigue of green revolution. *Proc. II Asia Pacific conference on agricultural biotechnology, Madras.*

Tayade, D.S. 1978. Possibilities of sericulture in Marathwada. Abs. 1st AU India Symp. On Sericultural Sciences. 4.

Tayade, D.S. 1981. Annual Report of MAU, Parbani.

Tayade, D.S. 1983. The feasibility and profitability of mulberry silkworm *Bombyx mori L.* under Marathwada condition. *Res Bull MAU* Parbhani 7, 53-58.

Tayade, D.S. 1987. Performance of different races of silkworm *Bombyx mori L.* under Marathwada condition. *Sericologia*, 27(3), 381-389.

Tayade, D.S. 1991. The development and promotion of sericulture in Maharashtra state. *Sericologia*, 31(1), 61-67.

Tayade, D.S. and Jawale, M.D. 1984. Studies on the comparative performance of silkworm races against different varieties of mulberry under Marathwada conditions. *Sericologia*, 24, 361-364.

Tayade, D.S., Jawale, M.D. and Unchegaonkar, P.K. 1986. Evaluation of some improved strains of mulberry by feeding experiment under Marathwada condition. National Seminar on Prospects and Problems of Sericulture in India. March 27-30, 33.

Tayade, D.S., Jawale, M.D. and Unchegaonkar, P.K. 1988. Evaluation of some improved strains of mulberry feeding experiment under Marathwada conditions. *Indian J. Seric.*, 27(2).

Teli, V.S., Pawar, M.B., Patil, B.R., Kalbhor, S.E. 1984. Performance of some mulberry silkworm strains and hybrids. J. Maharashtra Agricultural Universities, 9(1), 112-114.

Teotia, R.S. Singh, K.P. and Sen, S.K. 1992. Sericulture can meet challenges of drought in drylands. *Indian Silk*, 31 (6), 40-44.

Tewary, P.K. and G. Subha Rao, 1990. Mulberry Bi-Products and their utilization. *Indian Silk*, 29, 43-44.

Thiagarajan, V. 1988. Effect of formaldehyde on the hatchability of silkworm eggs of *Bombyx mori* L. *Indian J. Seric*, 27, 42-44.

Thiagarajan. V., Sindagi, S.S., Amarnath, S.A. and Nagabhusana Rao, N.N. 1991. Need for a study on silkworm hybrids in different seasons. *Indian silk*, 45.

Thiagarajan, V., Sindagi, S.S., Bhargava, S.K. and Ramesh Babu, M. 1992. Field performance of two commercial hybrids (Pm × NB18 : Pm x NB$_4$D$_2$).

Thomas, P.S.S. 1990. National Sericultural Project at a glance, CSB, Bangalore India.

Thomas, Jacob, 1998. Sericulture Development in Uttar Pradesh *Indian Silk*, 37, 5-9.

Tikoo, B.L. 1989. Problems related to sericulture extension in North-Eastern States. Workshop on Sericulture Extension and Management, Central Sericultural Research and Training Institute, Mysore, 30-31 August, 1989.

Tikoo, B.L., M.L. Kapila and S. Krishnaswami, 1971. Large scale trials on the comparative performance of multivoltine x bivoltine hybrids of mulberry silkworm in Mysore State. *Indian J. Seric.*, 10, 1.

Trag, A.R., Shaneen, A., Malik, G.N. and Malik, F.A. 1991. Impact of adoption of package of practices in sericulture for high productivity in Jammu & Kashmir state. *Sericologia*, 31(1), 193-95.

Ullal, S.R. and Narsimhanna M.N. 1978. Hand book of sericulture, CSB, Bangalore, India.

Uma, H.P., Gowrammy, V., Bajpai, A.K. and Sinha, A.K. 1992. (CSRTI, Mysore). Silk handicrafts : source of lucrative earing. *Indian Silk*, 31 (8), 34-38.

Vago, C. 1959. Lenchainement des maladies chiz lis insects. *Anmis. Epiphyt*, p. 181.

Vender, Wulp, F.M. 1986. Parasitic muscidae from British India -3 *Tricholyga bombycis* Becher. Indian Museum Notes., 3 11-15.

Venugopal, V. 1994. Women in sustainable sericulture development. *Indian silk*, 33, 29-32.

Venugopala, Pilali, S. and Jolly, M.S. 1985. An evaluation on the quality of mulberry varieties raised under hill conditions and the crop results of *Bombyx mori* L. *Indian J. Seric*, 24(2), 48-52.

Venugopala, Pillai S. and S. Krishnaswami, 1987. Adaptability of silkworm, *Bombyx mori* L. to tropical conditions III. Studies on the effect of high temperature during later developmental stages of silkworm. *Indian J. Seric*, 16(1), 63-71.

Venugopala, Pillai, S., Krishnaswamy, S. and Kasiviswanathan, K. 1987. Growth studies in silkworm, *Bombyx mori* L. under tropical conditions II. Influences of agronomical methods of mulberry on the growth, cocoon crop and fecundity of silkworm. *Indian J. Seric*. 26(1), 32-45.

Vijaya Kumari, K.M., Himanthraj, M.T. and Rajan, R.K. 2001. Effect of feed cut in fifth instar on cocoon characters and disease incidence in silkworm *B. mori. Uttar Pradesh J. 2001*, 21(1), 1-4.

Vijayan, K., S.P. Chakraborti, B.N. Roy and S.K. Sen. 1998. West Bengal : Winter Hardy Mulberry variety : A need. *Indian Silk*, 37, 6-8.

Vindhya, G.S., Depta, S.K. Himantharaj, M.T. and Singh, G.B. 1996. An economical analysis and comparison of shoot and stand rearing of silkworm *B. mori. J. Seric.*, 4(1), 7-14.

Vineet Kumar, Himanthrais, M.T., Rajan, R.K., Mathur, V.B., Kamble, C.K. and Datta, R.K. 1994. Simple leaf preservation for young age silkworm rearing. *Indian silk,* 32(9), 20-21.

Vinod Kumar and K.V. Benchamin. 1990a. Evaluation of mulberry leaf quality under two systems of pruning for young and late age silkworm rearing. *Indian J. Seric,* 29 (1), 168-173.

Vinod Kumar and Benchamin, K.V. 1990b. Mulberry leaf quality under two systems of pruning for young and late age silkworm rearing. *Indian J. Seric,* 29(2), 168-173.

Vishwanath, A.P. and K. Krishnamurthy, 1982-83. Effect of foliar spray of micro-utrients on the larval development and cocoon characters of silkworm *Bombyx mori L. Indian J. Seric.,* 21-22, 1-6.

Vishwanath, Kannantha, Natraj, B., Bhargava, S.K. and Mugdum, 1989. Introduction of Mulberry Sericulture in Andaman and Nicobar Islands. Workshop on Sericulture Extension and Management Central Sericultural Reserch and Training Institute, Mysore, 30-31 August, 1989.

Visweswara Gowda, B.L. 1986. Adoption of package of packages of practices in Chawki Rearing of Mulberry Silkworm in some villages of Mysore district in Karnataka. National seminar on Prospects and Problems of Sericulture in India March 27-30, 5.

Yadav, B.R. 2002. Major Research highlights of CSBR & D institutions during 2001-2002. *Indian silk,* July, 27-28.

Yadav, G.S., Reddy, K.J., Murgod, S.B., Roy, G.C. and B.R.R.P. Sinha, 1997. Medicinal Tasar flora of Bhandara. *Indian SIlk,* 36, 34-37.

Yokayama, T. 1963. Sericulture. *Ann. Rev. Ent.* 8, 287-298.

Zaman, W.Z., Kamble, C.K. and Singh, G.P. 1995. Studies on the yield variation with P1 seed rearers (Bivoltine) in K.R. *Pet. J. Seric.,* 3(1), 26-30.

Zhang, B. 1986. A discussion on rearing techniques of mulberry silkworm in ancient agricultural book Essentials of Agriculture and Sericulture. *Canye Kexue,* 12(3), 171.

Zhuang, D.H., Liu, S.X. and Long, L. 1994. Sericultural production strategies in the 21st century". In Int. Conf. Seric. Global silk-scenario-2001, CSR & TI, Mysore, 25-29 Oct 1994, 11-12.

Zubayri, A.R. 1983. Studies on the growth and development of silkworm *B. mori.*, in relation to leaf quality at different system of planting and harvest. Dissertation submitted to C.S.R. & T.I., Mysore, for specialization training in silkworm rearing technology course.

INDEX